Warriors
and Worthies

Warriors and Worthies

ARMS AND ARMOR THROUGH THE AGES

Helmut Nickel, *Curator of Arms and Armor for The Metropolitan Museum of Art*

color photographs by Bruce Pendleton

black and white photographs courtesy of The Metropolitan Museum of Art

all objects pictured are in the collections of The Metropolitan Museum of Art

ATHENEUM   1971   NEW YORK

INTRODUCTION

From his earliest beginnings Man has had to fight for his survival. Therefore since earliest times some of a man's most prized possessions have been his weapons, and the oldest specialized craft in the history of human civilization is that of the smith, the maker of weapons for hunting and fighting. The things the early smith shaped with hammer and anvil with the help of the divine element, Fire, were regarded with reverent awe, because they were endowed not only with the power to destroy life—as weapons—but to preserve life too—as armor. Great care was taken to fashion these objects not only for efficiency, but for beauty as well.

This art of the armorer was so important that the ancient Greeks had a smith, Hephaistos, better known under his Roman name Vulcan, among their gods; and their goddess of wisdom and protectress of the arts, Pallas Athene, was always represented in full armor. Among all museums in the world the Metropolitan Museum of Art is best suited to give a full view on this aspect of human culture. Besides having one of the finest collections in existence of European arms and armor of the Middle Ages, it has outstanding examples from practically every single period of history on display—and, last but not least, it is still active in this field. Few people know that the steel helmet of the American GI is based on a design developed in the Metropolitan Museum's armor shop, thus following the ancient armorers' noble tradition of protecting life.

Warriors
and Worthies

MACEHEADS

ANCIENT EGYPT

With the rise of the earliest civilizations, in Egypt and in Mesopotamia, came the earliest armies. Egypt, around 3100 B.C., was
united into a powerful state by the first of the Pharaohs, Narmer;
and one of the earliest surviving works of Egyptian art cele-
brates one of his military victories. Quite obviously a civilized
state needed a well-organized army to keep its barbarian neighbors away.

The Egyptian soldiers used spears and bows (in several ancient languages the words for "Egyptians" and "archer" were
the same) as missiles, and bronze axes for close combat. Officers
carried maces with beautifully carved stone heads, both as
weapons and badges of rank. No body armor was worn; the only
protective arms were large shields covered with bull hide. The
warriors marched into battle under the standards of their *nome*
(provinces); later, regimental standards came into use.

Since the river Nile is the lifeline of Egypt, boats were of great importance, and Egypt had a navy as early as it had an army. The model of a ship from a nobleman's tomb shows its crew toiling at the oars, shields hung on the cabin roof. The relief of marching marines, smartly shouldering staves and bows in bow cases, illustrates another aspect of army life: the man in the center of the upper row is an early sergeant-major carrying pen, inkbox, and two rolled sheets of papyrus—no doubt, for lists in duplicate!

THE SUMERIANS (3000–2500 B.C.)

The other of the two earliest civilizations, Sumer in Mesopotamia, was not a single, united empire like Egypt, but was divided into many small city-states. Therefore the Sumerians waged war even more often than the Egyptians, especially among themselves. Military events were of great importance in their art. Their soldiers fought with spear and axe, covering themselves with huge shields, and—an important improvement—protected by helmets and body armor in the shape of big cloaks.

REIN RING

AXE

SPEARHEAD

4

The Sumerians were the first to use one of the great inventions of man, the wheel, for military purposes. Their first war chariots were heavy affairs rolling on four solid wheels, drawn by four onagers (a species of wild ass) because the horse was not yet tamed. These chariots were equipped with a high dashboard hung with a quiver for javelins. They were manned by a driver and a fighting man. In order to keep the reins from tangling, the men gathered them through a rein ring on the wagon tongue. Since the entire chariot was made of wood, these bronze rein rings are all that is left of them today. But small metal models of chariots show us how they looked. Sometimes the draft animals were bulls. Perhaps their horns were thought of as an additional weapon.

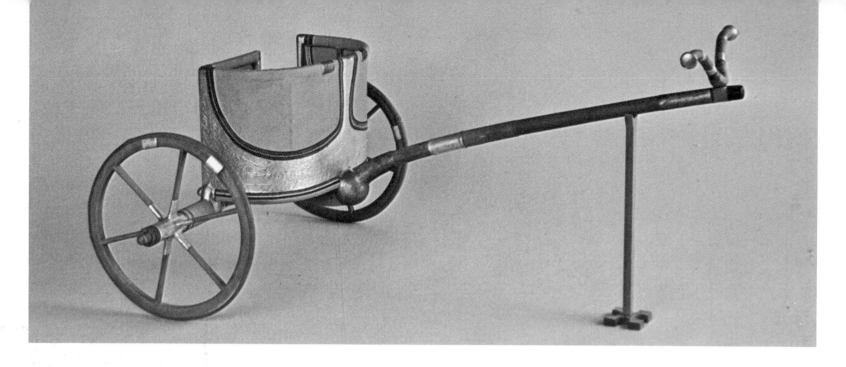

THE EGYPTIANS OF THE NEW KINGDOM

Around 1700 B.C. horsedrawn chariots appeared in Egypt, driven by a conquering people from the North, the Hyksos. The Egyptian infantry could not fight effectively against this new weapon, and the Hyksos—the "rulers of foreign countries"—ruled over the lands of the Nile for more than a century.

AXES

Unfortunately, when the Egyptians finally drove out the foreigners, they erased this blemish on their history so carefully that it is now impossible to say just who the Hyksos were. All that remained of them was their chariots, which the Egyptians copied and learned to use well.

These chariots were much lighter than the lumbering vehicles of the Sumerians; their swift-running wheels had four or six spokes, their bodies were hung with cases for bows and arrows. Two horses were harnessed to the yoke of the wagon tongue.

The ornamental breastplate in shape of a shield shows Pharaoh Amun-hotpe I—quiver slung over his back, battle-axe shouldered—leading two captives, a Northern Asiatic and a Southern Nubian, in the traditional pose of a victorious commander.

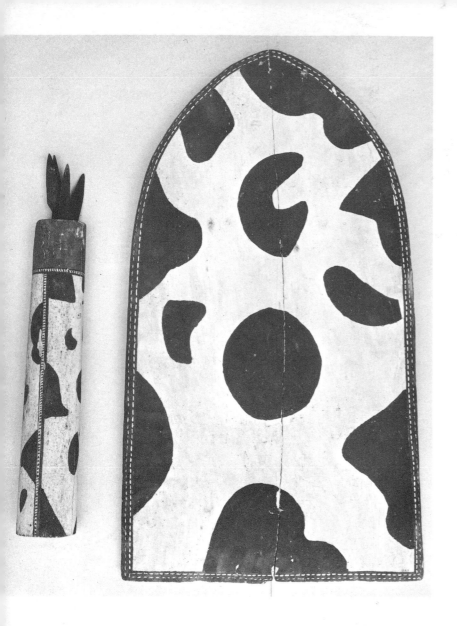

WEAPONS OF ANCIENT EGYPT

Thanks to the extremely dry climate of Egypt, an enormous number of objects that were put in tombs to serve their owners in the next world have survived to our times. Among these objects are many weapons, from the simple but graceful bows of common soldiers to the ornate but keen-edged daggers of generals and rulers.

Sometimes wooden replicas were substituted for the actual weapons, like the shield or the quiver shown here; but frequently real arms were used. The double-edged sickle-sword is cast in bronze and bears the name of its owner, Pharaoh Takelot. The blades of officers' battle-axes are real, and are decorated in skillfully modeled openwork often representing the troop's animal emblem. The mother-of-pearl badges engraved with the name of the pharaoh were worn by special troops. And "gold of valor", in the form of bracelets or necklaces, was given to distinguished warriors; pendants in the shape of lions were for courage, and in the shape of flies for persistence!

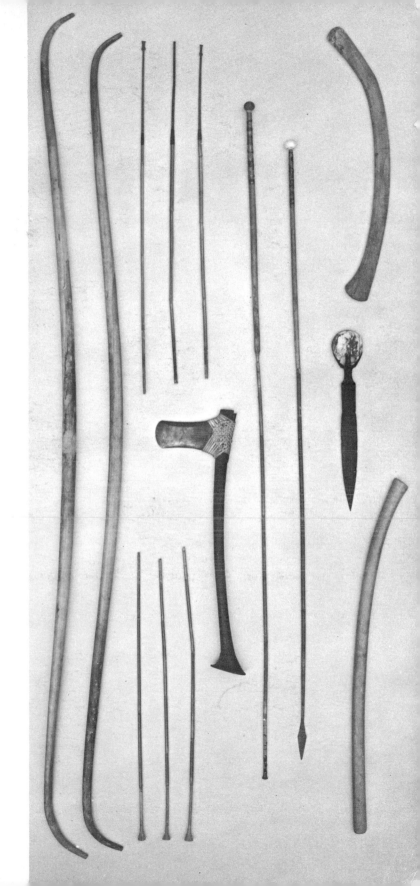

The collective picture shows two bows, six arrows, an axe, two lightweight throwing-spears or javelins—one with chisel-shaped flint tip, the other one with a pointed bronze head—a bronze dagger, and two boomerangs. The boomerangs and the reed arrows with club-shaped wooden heads were used for hunting, especially fowling, in order not to spoil the plumage with blood. The other three arrows and the first javelin have flint tips, with straight cutting edges, and were used in battle. Shield and mace or battle-axe were the components of the hieroglyph "to fight".

MOTHER-OF-PEARL
BADGE

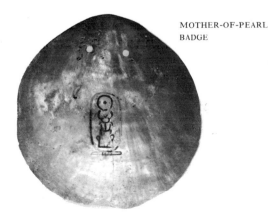

SEMITES AND HITTITES

North of Egypt, in Palestine and Syria, dwelt peoples who were divided into many different tribes, but who are known to us collectively as Semites. It is very likely that the Hyksos, who once succeeded in conquering Egypt, were a Semite tribe. The Semites appear in Egyptian art mostly as tribute bringers or as foes in defeat, as they are in the relief where they are shown struck down by the victorious Pharaoh's arrows. Many battles fought by the various Semitic peoples are familiar to us because they are mentioned in the Bible. Another people mentioned in the Bible are the Hittites, who lived farther north in what is now Turkey, though at times they extended their empire through Syria to the borders of Egypt. They were famous as charioteers. In production of weaponry, they seem to have been the first to make blades of iron.

HITTITE CHARIOT RELIEF

SYRIAN AXE

10

PEOPLES OF THE HIGHLANDS

To the north of Mesopotamia, in the mountains of what is today Iran, lived many small nations that were forgotten for thousands of years, whose cultures have only now come to light through the work of modern archaeologists.

The magnificent bronze helmet adorned with golden images of gods on its brow, and crested with a gold bird, must have been worked by the master craftsmen of Elam. Daggers with hilts of gold and alabaster and richly wrought axes have been found in Urartu and Luristan. From Luristan also come especially fine bronzes, such as the cheekpiece of a horse bit in the shape of a chariot, or the plaque engraved with a huntsman.

BABYLONIANS AND ASSYRIANS (1800–600 B.C.)

Because of the Bible everyone knows about the Babylonians and the Assyrians. They succeeded the Sumerians, but extended their boundaries far beyond the lands of Mesopotamia. Their warlike prowess was one of the main subjects of Assyrian art, and from these representations we know every detail of their warriors' appearance. The Assyrian army was the most efficient and formidable of its time. The Sumerians' favorite weapon was the spear, but the Assyrians used the bow, an even more advanced one than the Egyptians used. They had light chariots for two horses and two men, and heavy chariots for three horses and up to four men; but the really important tactical innovation they made was the use of archers on horseback, the beginning of cavalry. They also introduced the extensive use of body armor. Every soldier had a conical bronze helmet with cheekpieces. Units were distinguished from each other by their helmet crests.

Most soldiers also wore a cuirass of bronze scales laced together with leather thongs, a strong but flexible protection for charioteers and archers who could not easily handle shields.

Some of the swords of the Assyrians were curved like the one illustrated here. This one is inscribed with the name of King Adad-Nirari (12th century B.C.) in cuneiform characters.

The art of fortification was highly developed in the ancient Near East; but no city's walls could stand against the efficient engineers of Assyria, who built siege ramps on which assault troops could advance to scale the walls with storming ladders or flood through breaches laid by battering rams.

PLAQUES OF SIEGES, SHOWING
STORMING LADDERS AND WALLS AND TURRETS

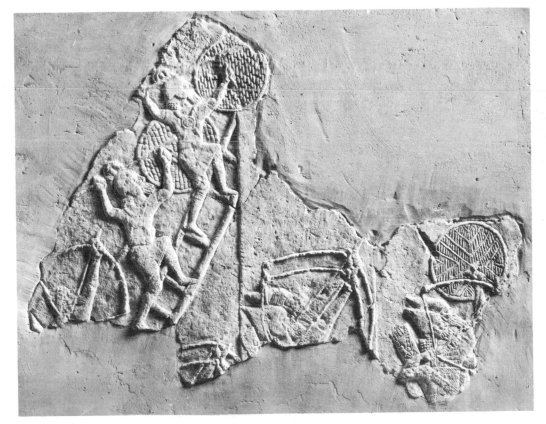

VASE SHOWING
MYCENAEAN CHARIOT

THE MYCENAEANS
(1500–1200 B.C.)

The first civilizations in Europe arose on the island of Crete and in the southern part of Greece. Dazzling treasures have been found in Mycenae, the capital of the kings sung about in Homer's *Iliad*. Its story is about the siege of the city of Troy, where the greatest heroes of the Achaeans—as these early Greeks called themselves—fought for ten years to rescue the beautiful Helen. Homer describes in great detail the splendid weapons of his heroes, and many like them have been uncovered in places Homer mentioned. Here appears for the first time the long sword, straight-bladed and double-edged, fit for cut and thrust. Many of them have bronze blades magnificently inlaid with figures in gold and silver.

14

For protection the Mycenaeans wore huge cowhide shields, either rectangular—in the words of Homer "like a tower"—or in a figure-eight form. Only the greatest lords seem to have worn bronze armor, but several types of helmets were known, mostly of leather mounted with bronze studs, or—as Homer tells us, too—reinforced with close-set rows of boars' tusks.

Chariots were prized possessions, but the broken country did not permit their use in intricate military maneuvers; in war they were usually only a means of transportation from camp to battlefield, where the heroes dismounted and fought on foot.

The Trojan War furnished scenes for artists to picture for centuries to come, such as the Death of Achilles and the Trojan Horse, as shown on these later seal stones.

BRONZE SWORDS

NORTH EUROPEAN BRONZE AGE CULTURES (1500–800 B.C.)

To the north of Greece, in the dense forests of Northern Europe, there dwelt a number of tribes whose cultures were rather similar, though they presumably spoke different languages. At the time of the Mycenaeans and other early Greeks these northern people had just emerged from the Stone Age, and some of their weapons and tools were still made of stone. Their most important tool, which served as a weapon as well, was the bronze axe. Its blade, without a socket, was directly derived from the stone axe. These "celts" were inserted in the cleft end of a knee-shaped handle. Later the celt was given a hollow socket, which fitted over the short end of the handle.

Though these peoples found it difficult to improve on the design of their old stone axe, they did find a way to perfect a weapon they had received from their southern neighbors, the sword. The early Mycenaean sword for all its splendor had a structural weakness—its blade was merely riveted to the lower part of the hilt. The swords developed in the North had a tang that extended through the whole length of the hilt, and gave it the firmness needed for a slashing blow.

BRONZE AXEHEADS

16

EARLY GREEKS
(1100–750 B.C.)

After the fall of the Mycenaean civilization there came a period of simpler artistic expression. Almost all surviving works of art from this time are pottery, painted in geometric patterns, often with rows of stylized warriors. These warriors still carry a large shield, similar to the figure-eight shield of the Mycenaeans, a sword, and two short spears. Long feather or horsehair crests stream from their helmets. Noblemen ride their chariots, and many-oared ships with wicked battering rams and staring eyes at their prows loom among the marching warriors.

VASE SHOWING GREEK FOOT SOLDIERS

THE GREEKS
(700–300 B.C.)

With the rise of the Greek city-states, the old army with its highborn leader thundering off in his chariot ahead of his lightly armed men, was replaced by the *phalanx*, the close-rank infantry formation of citizen-soldiers. In the city state it was both the right and the duty of a citizen to bear arms for his city, and the development of these well-organized armies of foot soldiers played an important part in the rise of Greek democracy.

BRONZE HORSEMAN

The Greek word for this heavily armed foot soldier was *hoplite*, which means "shield bearer". His main protection was a shield of oxhide, usually circular. The Greek shield was carried by a central strap for the forearm—an innovation that made its weight easier to handle—and a grip for the hand; its face was painted or applied with distinctive devices, sometimes alike for whole units, sometimes different for individual fighters. The shield covered the man from chin to knee, and additional care was taken to protect the exposed parts, head and legs.

19

SPEAR BUTT

ILLYRIAN HELMET

Greek helmets were made in a number of designs, all of them beautifully shaped and skillfully hammered from a single sheet of bronze. Crested combs were added as an extra protection against sword strokes and as a decoration. The simplest helmet form was conical, a translation into metal of the ordinary felt hat, the *pilos*—favored by the austere Spartans. The most elaborate was the so-called Corinthian helmet that enclosed the whole head in a smooth shell, leaving only open slits for eyes and mouth. The other element of armor worn by all was a pair of bronze greaves, which encased the leg from knee to ankle and fit so exactly that they needed no straps or buckles.

CHALCIDIAN HELMET

SPARTAN HELMET

CORINTHIAN HELMET

20

Body armor was either a bronze cuirass, consisting of breast and backplate that covered the upper body to the waist, or a corselet of leather or thick layers of linen.

The principal weapons were a thrusting spear about ten feet in length, and a sword for hand-to-hand combat. Archers and slingers supported the ranks of spearmen. The bristling spears and dense wall of shields made the phalanx a formidable enemy on land, and also on shipboard, where hoplites fought as marines. Greek warships are among the most beautiful craft ever designed.

THE PERSIANS (600–300 B.C.)

The most worthy foe the Greeks encountered—at Marathon, Thermopylae, Salamis, Issus—were the Persians. They had erected an Empire that covered most of the known world of the time, stretching from India to the Aegean Sea and Ethiopia. Warriors from many nations swelled the ranks of the Persian army. The backbone of this army was its splendid cavalry. The cavalrymen wore little or no armor, in order not to encumber themselves or weigh down their horses; but their voluminous clothes were gaily colored and glittered with gold jewelry.

PERSIAN HORSEMAN

LION HEAD MOUNTS

GOLD ROUNDEL WITH LIONS

The favorite weapon of the Persians was the heavy composite bow; archery was so important that the Great Kings had themselves portrayed as archers on their coins. A Persian boy had to learn three things above all: horsemanship, archery, and to tell the truth! Other weapons included a short sword tied to the right thigh and short spears for throwing and stabbing. These spears had a metal ball at the butt as a counterweight to the blade; the elite corps, the Ten Thousand Immortals, had balls made of gold and silver on their spears.

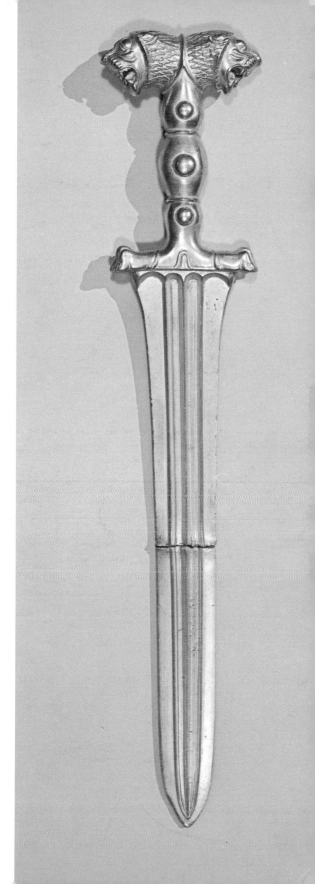

THE PHOENICIANS AND CYPRIOTS
(700–300 B.C.)

In a series of harbor towns scattered around the Mediterranean Sea lived the Phoenicians, who still enjoy the reputation of being the best sailors of antiquity. Their ships went as far north as the mist-shrouded Tin Islands (Cornwall); and to the south they succeeded in circumnavigating Africa at least once. These dauntless seamen had to be tough fighters to survive such dangerous trips. Unfortunately for us they spent so much time sailing and trading that they left few works of art behind to tell us how they looked.

Small votive statuettes and scenes from sarcophagi show us that in addition to navies they had chariots, cavalry, infantry and even war elephants. Their spearmen carried Greek-style shields, and their archers apparently fought in teams with a shield bearer for protection, a tactical device they learned from the Assyrians. The conical helmets or hats of the figures illustrated are typically Phoenician.

THE SCYTHIANS (700–200 B.C.)

In the steppes to the north of the Black Sea roamed the nomadic Scythians. They were related to the Persians and were even greater horsemen. As nomads the Scythians had no use for statuary or other large scale art that might show us their likenesses, but some of their weapons—like the gold scabbard for a short sword—are decorated with lively scenes. Here we see bearded Scythians in baggy trousers, armed with sword and battle-axe, fighting against Greeks; the realistic style indicates that this work of art was made by a Greek artist for some great Scythian chieftain. An iron battle-axe with a silver socket shows the type of animal decoration favored by the Scythian metalworkers.

THE ETRUSCANS
(750–250 B.C.)

Perched on the hilltops of Central Italy were the walled cities of the Etruscans. Like all ancient peoples, they buried their dead with all their wealth for use in the Other World. Therefore we are quite well informed about the things they used in daily life, though much of their language still remains a mystery.

HELMET WITH
CHEEKPIECES

DETAIL OF ETRUSCAN CHARIOT

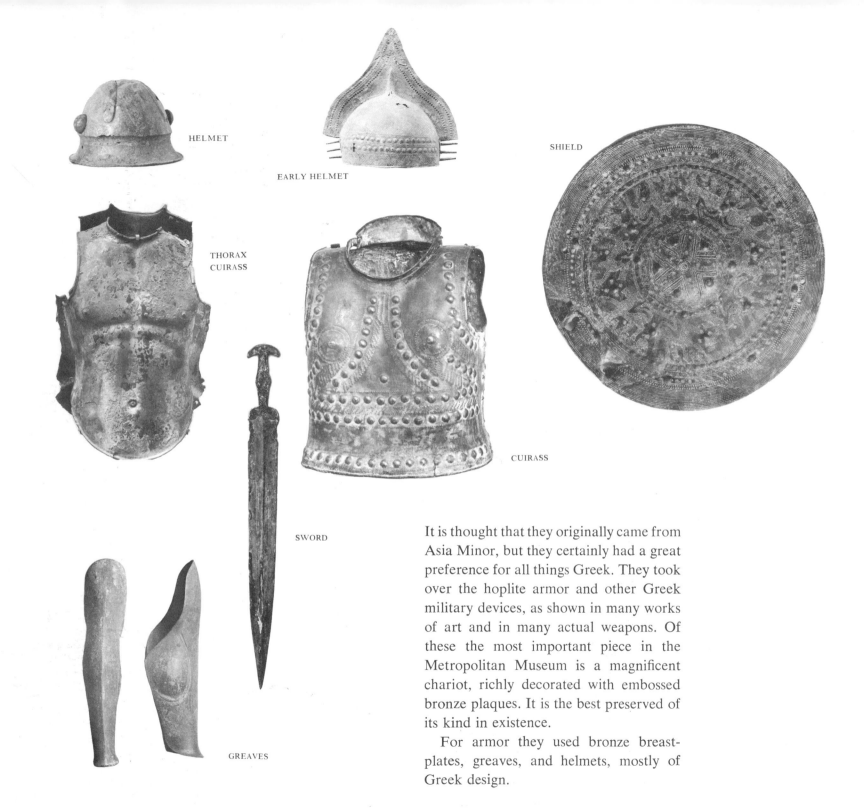

HELMET

EARLY HELMET

SHIELD

THORAX
CUIRASS

CUIRASS

SWORD

GREAVES

It is thought that they originally came from Asia Minor, but they certainly had a great preference for all things Greek. They took over the hoplite armor and other Greek military devices, as shown in many works of art and in many actual weapons. Of these the most important piece in the Metropolitan Museum is a magnificent chariot, richly decorated with embossed bronze plaques. It is the best preserved of its kind in existence.

For armor they used bronze breast-plates, greaves, and helmets, mostly of Greek design.

These are shown in the bronze group of a warrior supporting his wounded companion, and on the plaques of the chariot.

THE ROMANS

Rome was a city-state that eventually conquered and ruled most of the known world. Its well-trained legions marched over the foggy glens of northern Britain and through the burning sands of Egypt, from the Straits of Gibraltar to the shores of the Black Sea. Originally their arms and equipment were similar to those of their neighbors, the Etruscans, but soon they developed their own.

Instead of the long thrusting-spear, they used a heavy javelin, the *pilum*. This was a throwing-spear of peculiar construction: its small barbed head was attached to its wooden shaft by a long rodlike iron socket.

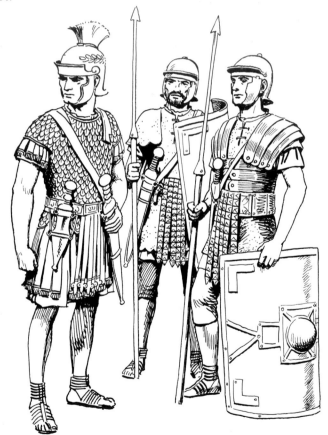

When this missile was hurled in a volley at the enemy, it was dangerous even if it only hit a shield, because its barbed head stuck fast and could not be pried out in a hurry. In addition, the iron rod of the socket prevented the enemy from hacking it off in order to free his shield from the dragging weight of the shaft. Furthermore, the impact usually bent the iron rod, rendering the pilum useless for the enemy, who might otherwise have thrown it right back.

The final onslaught in battle was made with the short sword, the *gladius,* with the warrior protected by the big rectangular shield, the *scutum.* The gladius was worn on the right side, so it could be easily drawn, unhampered by the shield. As body armor the legionary wore a bronze helmet, with a crest indicating unit and rank, and a leather jerkin reinforced with strips of metal. Officers wore elaborate bronze cuirasses and decorated helmets.

The Roman legions were aided in tactical maneuvers by their extensive use of distinctive battle standards that served as rallying points or signaling instruments. Each legion was made up of ten cohorts, comparable to our companies, and each cohort carried its own standard, the *signum,* on a long staff.

CARLE VERNET, *Triumph of Paulus Aemilius*

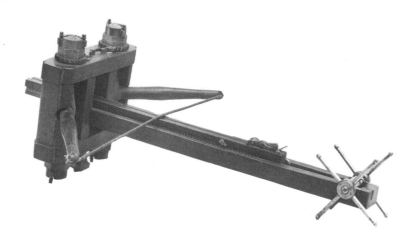

Being excellent engineers, the Romans built many engines for siege and field: battering rams, ballistae for throwing rocks, and catapults for hurling large darts. Throwing engines were powered by torsion and tension of levers stuck in thick bundles of ropes and pulled tight in frames, as seen in the reconstructed catapult.

Actual Roman weapons and armor have come down to us in very small numbers. Unlike the Greeks and Etruscans, who laid a dead warrior into his grave with all his arms, the Romans buried their legionaries without weapons. Each man's arms went back to the depot to be repaired and issued to the next recruit.

From statues and other works of art, however, we know how these celebrated soldiers looked. And their fame, together with the awe the works of art inspired, lead even present-day artists to turn to Roman armor if they want to represent heroic costume.

BRONZE, ROMAN AND BARBARIAN

THE CELTS

Among the most valiant enemies the Roman legions had to fight were the Celts. They lived in what is now France, Spain, the British Isles, North Italy, and some of them even in Turkey. Fierce warriors, they fought on foot—their nobles sometimes on horseback—wielding long iron swords. Unfortunately, their technology was not quite up to forging a good blade; and therefore we hear from Roman sources that after a particularly heavy sword stroke, the Celtic warrior might have to step back behind the battle line and straighten out his sword under his foot. Very few of them had helmets or body armor; most of them went to battle naked above the waist, their long hair greased and combed straight up, in order to give it a bristling appearance. Their only defense was an oval wooden shield, often made with fine bronze mountings. Common to all Celts were torques, heavy neck rings of silver or gold, worn by fighting men as badges of honor.

TORQUES, SPEAR MOUNTINGS AND BUCKLE

THE BARBARIANS

In the North and the East of Europe, beyond the borders of the Roman Empire, dwelt the barbarians, mostly tribes that spoke Germanic tongues. These tribes were a warlike lot. Even their names were often derived from their weapons. The Saxons, for example, were named after their machete-like long-knife "sax"; and the Langobards after their "long axes". The Germanic tribes fought mostly on foot, with spears and swords and with wooden hidebound shields as their only armor. They were fiercely loyal to their chieftains, and this and their fighting spirit made up for their poor equipment.

However, in the year 375 A.D. a new type of warrior appeared on the European battlefields. From the steppes of Central Asia came nomad horsemen, the Huns and Avars. Their riders were not only armored, but they possessed an important innovation in horsemanship, the stirrup.

The first of the Germanic tribes to encounter the Huns were the Goths, and they were quick to adopt the new equipment. Soon Goths, Burgundians, and Franks were sporting heavy armor and glittering *spangenhelms,* made of metal but patterned after the felt cap of the Asian nomads, and were nailing bright pieces of cloth as banners to their lance shafts, in imitation of the fluttering pennants the Huns had brought with them.

Eventually the Barbarians conquered many Roman lands, and when the Franks took over the Roman cities in the Rhinelands, with their important metalworkers' shops, they began producing mail armor (probably a Celtic invention) and sword blades that became famous for centuries to come.

SPANGENHELM, SHIELD BOSS AND SWORD

Out of this blending of cultures, the combination of Hunnish horsemanship and weapons with the code of honor and loyalty of the Germanic tribes, emerged a fighting man who in time developed into the medieval knight.

The barbarians did not produce any statues and paintings; their art forms were song and poetry, and it was in this period that the historical persons lived who later became glorified in the great heroic poems: King Arthur, Beowulf, Siegfried and Hagen, Dietrich von Bern, Wayland the Smith.

CHATELAINE

BUCKLE

CHATELAINE

BUCKLE

BUCKLE

THE BYZANTINES

The Western part of the Roman Empire was dissolved by the Barbarians in 476 A.D.; but the Eastern Empire, Byzantium, held out for nearly one thousand more years. Defending the empire was a professional army, whose men were called soldiers after the *solidus* the gold piece that was used to pay their wages.

Byzantine art was mostly religious in nature, therefore we depend for pictures of warriors almost exclusively on Biblical scenes and images of military saints, such as St. George or St. Demetrius.

SOLIDI

The dress and equipment of the Byzantine soldiers were based on those of the Roman legions, but had, of course, many characteristics of their own. Their body armor was a cuirass of scales with shoulder pieces and a crested helmet; each unit had its own distinctive color. Banner and shields were emblazoned with Christian symbols. The Byzantine army must have been a truly splendid and colorful sight. Gilding and precious stones embellished the arms of officers and elite troops, heavy neck rings were worn as badges of honor.

IVORY PLAQUE SHOWING BYZANTINE SOLDIERS

The main arm of the Byzantine army was the heavy cavalry, fully armored and equipped with both lance and bow. The infantry fought partly with spear and shield in close formation, partly with archers and slingers. Especially formidable was the Byzantine navy, which ruled the Eastern Mediterranean Sea for centuries without being seriously challenged. Its most dreaded weapon was the famous Greek Fire, probably a mixture containing naphtha and sulphur, which could burn even on the water and was practically unextinguishable. Its formula was such a closely guarded state secret that it was lost when Byzantium finally fell with the capture of its capital, Constantinople—now Istanbul—by the Turks in 1453.

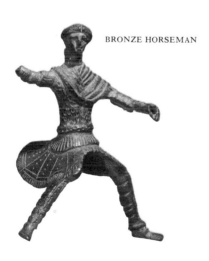

BRONZE HORSEMAN

ST. DEMETRIUS

39

THE SASANIANS

The primary foes of the Byzantines on their Eastern border were the Persian Sasanians. They considered themselves the rightful heirs of the ancient Persians who had battled the Greeks and been overthrown by Alexander the Great (332-323 B.C.). After the downfall of Alexander's successors, another tribe, the Parthians, had ruled for a while and fought the Romans; but they were defeated in turn by the Sasanians in 224 A.D. Like all Iranians, the Sasanians were great horsemen; and their army was chiefly a cavalry of heavily armed riders. These *cataphractarii,* with their mail and scale armor for man and horse and armament of lance, bow, and sword, were copied by the Byzantine cavalry. Most of the representations of Sasanian fighting men are huge reliefs carved into living rock, which cannot be pictured here.

SILVER BOWL

SEALSTONE

COPPER BOWL

However on seals, coins and other small objects we can see them in their baggy trousers—trousers being always the typical costume for nations of horsemen—and tall helmet-like hats. Sasanians were also great hunters, and their artists created beautiful silver bowls showing their kings in pursuit of fleet or fearsome animals.

The Sasanian Empire came to an end in 651 A.D. when it was overrun by Arabs fired by fanatical zeal for their new religion, Islam; however the Persian national epic *Shah Nahmeh,* composed in the thirteenth century, celebrated Bahram Gur, Khosro, and other Sasanian kings.

41

EARLY CHINA

The riders of the steppes who swept into Europe, and helped to topple the crumbling Roman Empire, harassed the villages and towns of an ancient civilization at the other end of the world too, of China. Though more interested in the peaceful arts of agriculture and learning, the Chinese had to take steps to fight off the intruders. One of these steps was the erection of the Great Wall of China (begun in the 3rd century B.C.), and the other the organization of troops of horsemen that could tackle the raiders better than the infantry and chariot armies they had had.

The influence of the steppe nomads on the arms and armor of the Chinese can be seen in the swords here illustrated. They are nearly identical in shape to those found among the weapons of the Huns and Avars. The armor of the Chinese troopers was either a cuirass of metal or bone scales laced together (like that of their enemies), or a corselet with large shoulder pieces of moulded leather, usually water buffalo or rhinoceros hide. Since the cavalrymen were mostly archers, they carried only small round shields or more often none at all; but the infantryman, whose armor more often than not was only a thickly quilted jacket, used a large shield for protection. The horses too were protected against the enemies' arrowstorms by chamfrons and heavy trappings.

IRON HELMET

EARLY JAPAN

The Japanese have always considered weapons to be among their most precious possessions. Thus for a long time a man's arms followed him into his grave. But in the sixth century A.D. a thrifty emperor decreed that this custom was to be discontinued because too many good weapons were thus lost. This was unfortunate for those who wanted peace then, and for archaeologists who search for old weapons now. The Metropolitan Museum is one of the very few places outside of Japan itself that is able to show early Japanese arms and armor. Helmets were built of narrow strips of steel riveted together; the same type of construction was used for the cuirasses, which covered three-quarters of the body with one piece, and had a separate piece closing the gap at the left side. As a protection against an arrow from behind, the back of the cuirass was drawn up in a high sweep to guard the neck. Another type of helmet was constructed with lames of steel radiating from a knob on its top; this *Kando Maru Hachi* must have derived from Chinese and Mongolian forms of the spangenhelm. From China, too, came the first treasured swords, but very soon the Japanese craftsmen produced blades that surpassed those of their teachers.

IRON CUIRASS

KANDO MARU HACHI HELMET

THE EARLY MIDDLE AGES

From among the Germanic tribes that helped destroy the Romans, the Franks emerged as the mightiest. Under their greatest ruler, Charlemagne, they founded the Holy Roman Empire in 800 A.D. thinking to revive the great Roman civilization. The Frankish system of government was feudalism, rule by a warrior aristocracy bound in loyalty to an overlord. The mark of an aristocrat was the ability to own a horse and ride into battle. In most European languages the word for horse is the root of the word that signifies a knight; *chevalier* in French, *cavaliere* in Italian, *caballero* in Spanish are derived from *cheval, cavallo* and *caballo;* the German *Ritter* means *rider.* The earliest knights were armored in mail shirts, conical helmets, and round shields, with lance and sword for weapons. Soon they discovered, however, that the smashing thrust of a lance couched under the arm could best be parried by a shield covering the whole left side of the fighter from chin to knee; and the old circular shield was abandoned in favor of an elongated form, ending in a point. The work of art that perhaps symbolizes this period most perfectly is the *Song of Roland* celebrating Charlemagne's champion, his sword Durendal, and his horn Olifant.

HELMET WITH
NOSE GUARD

OLIPHANT

SPUR

SEAL SHOWING
ELONGATED SHIELD

45

THE VIKINGS

His sword and his ship were the things dearest to the heart of a Norseman in the ninth and tenth century. They were regarded almost as living beings, were given names and treated with superstitious respect. A good sword had to be sharp and unbreakable; which posed a difficult problem for the smith. If the steel was hard enough to hold a keen edge, it was brittle; and if iron was tough enough not to break at a heavy blow, it was too soft and easily dulled. Therefore the swordsmiths invented an elaborate method of forging blades from innumerable strands of steel and iron hammered together to give them both hardness and flexibility. But even such a sword with a "pattern-welded" blade might be blunted by a magic spell; so it was a natural precaution to use silver in its decoration, because silver was thought to repel magic. The Vikings are familiar to everyone with their dragon ships and horned helmets. The burial mounds of Norwegian and Swedish sea kings have yielded whole ships and splendid helmets among their enormous treasures, but strangely not one of these helmets has had horns.

VIKING SWORD

THE CRUSADES AND THE AGE OF CHIVALRY

The most famous events of the Middle Ages are the Crusades. The first of them started in 1096, and the eighth and last ended in 1271. Almost everyone has heard the names of their heroes: Geoffrey of Bouillon, Richard the Lion-Hearted, Frederick Barbarossa, and Saint Louis.

CRUSADER'S MAP

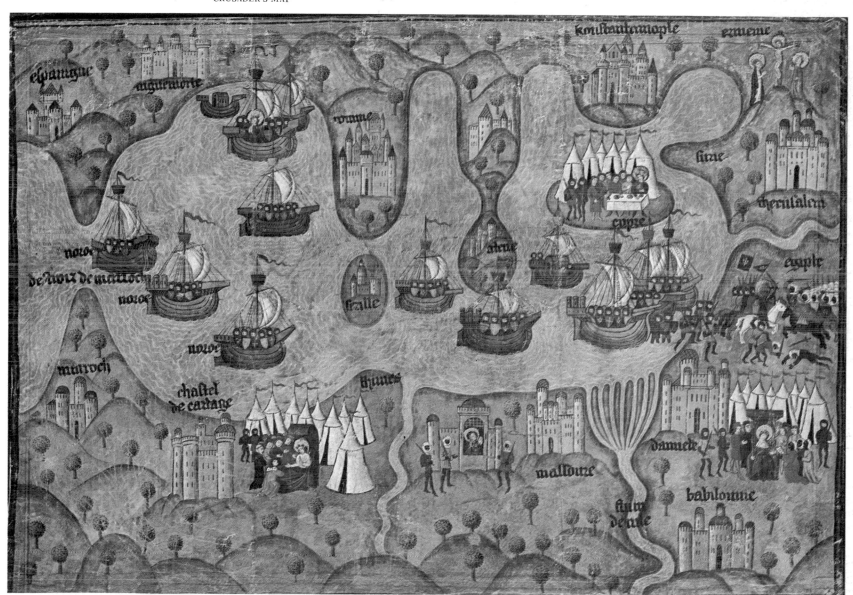

One of the questions inevitably asked by a visitor to an armor collection is, "Where is the crusaders' armor?" Unfortunately, there is none left. The knights' shirts of mail and their wooden shields have fallen to rust and dust; of their conical helmets with outjutting noseguards, barely half a dozen have survived. However, one of the few objects that unquestionably have been on a crusade is the sword pommel here illustrated. It was found in Damascus and bears the arms of Peter de Dreux, Duke of Brittany, one of the leaders of Saint Louis' crusade, 1249.

Contact with the culturally superior Eastern world brought an entirely new sophistication to the rough-and-ready knights of the West. They acquired a taste for exotic spices and fruit, and ideas for more gracious living in their grim castles. Eastern ideals of chivalry—fighting to right wrongs, protection of the weak, generosity to defeated foes, and especially courtesy and service to ladies—were accepted and refined to a degree where the perfect knight was expected to handle sword and lance, lute and chessboard with equal skill. Campaigning in the Holy Land taught the crusaders to cover armor and helmet against the scorching rays of the desert sun; and when they returned to their homelands, bringing with them the rich fabrics of the East, they kept surcoat, helmet mantling, and horse trappings for decorative value.

SWORD POMMEL

LADY'S TOKEN

BRONZE EFFIGY KNIGHT

For protection against the arrow storm of the Saracens, gradually a helmet was developed that covered the whole head, leaving only narrow eye slits for the knight to peer through. At the same time the shield became flattened at the top, since an upcurve was no longer necessary to protect the face. The new triangular shape of the shield became symbolic of the Trinity, just as the cruciform sword hilt had already taken on religious significance for the Christian Knight.

IVORY CROSS,
WITH DETAIL

49

HERALDIC ANIMALS

Eagle

Griffin

Lion

Unicorn

Leopard

Dragon

HERALDIC DIVISIONS AND FIGURES

divided per fess

divided per pale

chevron

fesse

pale

quarterly

bend

HERALDRY

In the twelfth century with the introduction of the pot helmet, the individual knight could no longer be recognized by his face, and another means of identification became necessary. So the large surface of the shield was painted with a distinctive emblem. These "cognizances" became hereditary marks of certain families, or symbols of offices and fiefs. In order to make sure that they were recognizable from a distance, they were painted in boldly contrasting colors. These colors were limited to red, blue, black, white, yellow, and—less commonly—green and purple. Of these, white and yellow were called silver and gold or "metals"; and the basic rule of heraldry (the art of composing a coat-of-arms, named after the heralds, the officials in charge of tournaments) was that one of the metals should be combined with one of the other colors; two metals or two colors could not be used together. Many of the oldest arms are simple geometric patterns made up of a metal and a color, but because armorial bearings were designed for battle, arms displaying fierce animals such as lions, boars and dragons were, of course, much in favor also. Sometimes a coat-of-arms was derived from a much older symbol. The White Horse of Kent and of Hanover was originally a totem animal of the Saxons; the Dragon of Wales was a Roman ensign and the Eagle of the Holy Roman Empire was the eagle of Jupiter, used on the battle standard of the Roman legions.

The helmet—which after all was the cause of these developments—soon was topped by a crest that became the other half of what was known as "full" arms. Sometimes the crest repeated the emblem on the shield, sometimes it was entirely different.

Heraldic bearings were originally designed to identify the fighting man, the knight, but they soon became a status symbol. Burghers of the cities and other commoners strove to acquire arms, but not all of them succeeded. Many people today think that every family owns a coat-of-arms, or that all families with the same name are entitled to the use of arms granted to any one of them. Unfortunately, this is not so. Coats-of-arms are a one-family business; and it is quite likely that at some time someone might have been granted arms that he could forward to his heirs, but that his cousin and even his brothers could have had no share in.

HERALDIC FLOWERS

Fleur-de-Lys (Iris)

Rose

THREE HERALDS' BADGES

XIV CENTURY ARMOR AND THE HUNDRED YEARS' WAR

The mail armor of the Crusades was flexible and strong. It would protect against a sword cut, but not absorb the shock of the blow. A padded garment worn underneath and a shield were the shock breakers, but they could be quite cumbersome at times. And arrows, and especially crossbow bolts, could pierce through the rings of the mail, as knights discovered to their dismay in the Hundred Years' War (1337-1453). To remedy this, armorers tried to find ways to create rigid defenses with glancing surfaces that would deflect the points of deadly weapons. At first knees and lower legs were encased in shaped steel plates, because these were the most exposed parts in the press of battle; and soon there were similar protections for arms, elbows, and shoulders. The real problem, however, was to invent an efficient protection for the trunk, breast and abdomen. The knights, used to loose-fitting mail shirts, were reluctant to be encased in rigid steel plates, so armorers invented a sleeveless jacket lined with small iron plates. These were riveted to the fabric, with the rivets showing on the outside in a decorative pattern. The breast plates sometimes had chains to which sword and dagger could be attached, to avoid losing them in battle. Other chains secured the helmet and shield.

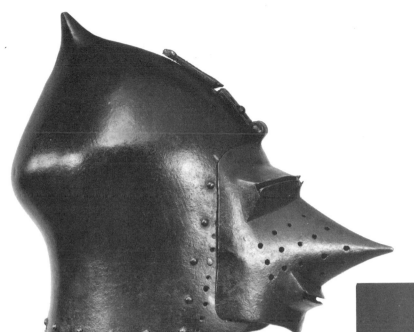

The big helmets that might have given many knights claustrophobia were gradually abolished for "hounskulls", close-fitting steel caps with pointed visors that could be flicked open for easier breathing. Ambitious armorers started designing armor for the knights' chargers too, steel chanfrons for their heads, and mail trappings for their bodies. With his legs encased in steel, the knight now practically stood in his stirrups, perched on an over-high saddle. To reach his horse, his spurs—his badges of rank—became longer and longer.

53

XV CENTURY ARMOR AND THE HUNDRED YEARS WAR

By about 1400 the triangular knightly shield had gone out of fashion; the new shield had a special cutout in its side to rest the lance in. A historically interesting piece is the plain helmet, which is thought to have been worn by Joan of Arc. When she was wounded in the head by a crossbow bolt during the siege of Orléans (1430), she dedicated the helmet that had saved her life to a church there. The helmet you see here hung in that church for centuries—and you can see the hole from a crossbow bolt.

TYROLEAN TARGE (SHIELD)

KING ARTHUR TAPESTRY

ST. GEORGE (SILVER)

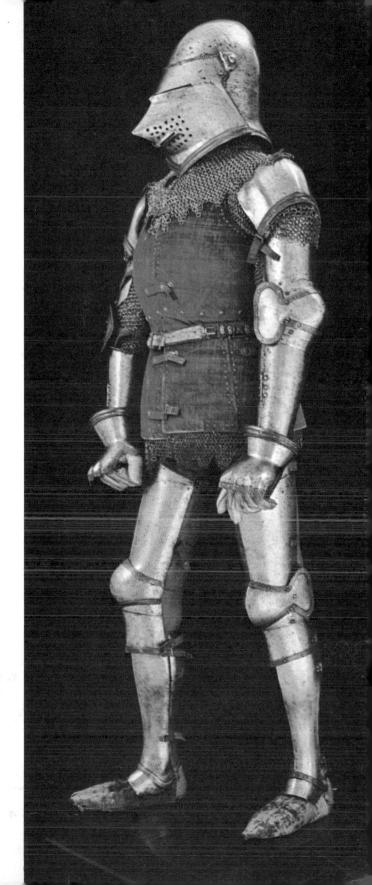

GOTHIC ARMOR,
BACK VIEW

PLATE ARMOR OF
THE XV CENTURY

By the middle of the fifteenth century, the process of encasing the body of the knight in a practically invulnerable shell of steel was completed. The shield had been discarded as unnecessary, and, most important of all, the cuirass and the helmet fitted body and head closely. The breastplate was still made of an upper and a lower part, held together by a central stud. This allowed for some movement of the torso. The helmets were either *armets,* with hinged cheekpieces closing at the chin and a pivoted visor covering the face, or *sallets,* with a long tail protecting the neck and a special guard for the chin, the *bevor.* The armet had a disc on a short stem attached to the nape of the neck, as a shock absorber for blows there; this was called the *rondelle.* The solid breast plate made possible the introduction of the lance rest, a hook at the right side designed to take up the weight of the couched lance. In most cases the lance rest was hinged and could be folded upward out of the way when the knight had to wield his sword after the lance was broken.

ARMET

SALLET

56

This armor was worn during the civil war in England known as the Wars of the Roses, called after the heraldic emblems of the fighting parties: the red rose of Lancaster, and the white rose of York.

It has been said over and over that a knight's armor was so heavy he could not get up without help when thrown to the ground and he had to be hoisted into the saddle by a derrick. This is nonsense, of course, because it would have been simply suicidal to load oneself with hardware until movement was impossible. On the contrary, a full suit of armor weighed only about fifty to sixty pounds, no more than the battle pack of a modern soldier; with all parts carefully fitted on and distributed over the entire body, it could be worn with great ease. It was expected of the perfect knight that he be able to vault into the saddle of his horse in full armor without using the stirrups—an ability that must have come in handy when he had to mount a horse in the press of battle, after his first steed went down.

MACE   SWORD

GOTHIC ARMOR

This armor is named after the Gothic style of architecture, because its spiky appearance echoes the pointed arches, finials and turrets of the period. For functional beauty Gothic armor is equalled by few other things, even in this wonderful period when craftsmen had the uncanny knack of turning the most humble piece of furniture or crockery into a work of art.

The greatest armor-making center of the fifteenth century was Milan in Northern Italy. Entire sections of this city teemed with workshops; some of them were even mass-producing in the modern sense, with specialized workers for single elements of armor, such as helmets, elbow cops, or gauntlets. Each armorer struck his mark on the pieces he had worked on as a token of guarantee. Since several specialists often cooperated on one suit, it is not unusual to find different marks together. Of the many hundreds of armorers, some masters or even families of masters became widely known; the Missaglias and the Negroli were two such families. Kings and princes from all over Europe tried to persuade Milan masters to come to their courts to work.

ITALIAN ARMORERS' MARKS

MAXIMILIAN ARMOR

This armor is named after Emperor Maximilian, who was called "the Last of the Knights" for his chivalrous manners and his keen interest in armor. He established his court workshop at Innsbruck in the Tyrol, where armorers worked under his personal supervision. One of the innovations of the time—around 1500—that he favored, was the regular fluting of the surfaces; this gave the plates additional strength without increase in weight. At the same time the spiky outlines of Gothic armor gave way to rounded Renaissance forms.

Innsbruck Hallmark

Nürnberg Hallmark

Landshut Hallmark

Augsburg Hallmark

Jörg Seusenhofer

Kunz Lochner

Mathes Deutsch

Desiderius Colman Helmschmied

Adrian Treytz

Valentin Siebenbürger

Sigmund Wolf

Anton Peffenhauser

Hans Prunner

Matthäus Frawenpreiss

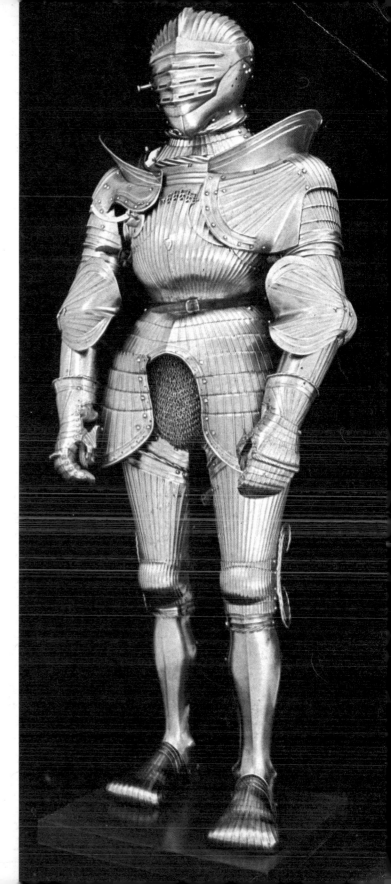

While Milan held an unchallenged international position as style setter (even today the word "milliner" is a reminder of this) in armor in the fifteenth century, in the early sixteenth century the German cities of Nürnberg, Augsburg, and Landshut came to the fore. The shops in these cities were much smaller than those in Milan and so the masters became better known as individuals.

Some of the armor they made shatters a common myth about armor: that people in the Middle Ages must have been much shorter than people today because the surviving suits of armor are so small. The truth is that Italian suits are likely to be relatively small, but so are Italians even today; on the other hand, some armor was made for men over six feet tall. Often armor was made for young men not yet fully grown. When they outgrew their first suits, these were still in good enough condition to be worth preserving. The suits they had later saw hard wear in camp and field and were often too worn to be preserved.

WOODCUT,
MAXIMILIAN ON HORSEBACK

FOOTSOLDIERS OF THE XV AND XVI CENTURIES: YEOMEN, HUSSITES AND SWISS

It was the humble foot soldier who brought into being the knight in shining armor, for plate armor was created as a defense against the crossbowman's bolts. Yet for a long time the foot soldiers themselves were no more than a poorly armed and poorly organized rabble. When cities began to grow, however, and—as in the ancient Greek city states—every burgher was expected to take part in the defense of his town, things began to change. As early as 1302 Flemish burghers scored a smashing victory over an army of proud French knights at Courtrai; soon afterward, in 1346, English longbowmen had their day at Crécy; and Swiss halberdiers and pikemen succeeded at Laupen in 1339 and Sempach in 1386.

The English yeomen usually fought in a defensive position, sending rapid sheets of arrows into ranks of charging knights; the Swiss worked in massed squares, attacking as a living avalanche that bristled with pikes and halberds, and with crossbowmen and the newly introduced handgunners on their flanks.

WOODCUT,
SWISS FOOTSOLDIERS

A combination of these tactics was used by still another group of successful foot soldiers, the Hussites. These Bohemian rebels used the *Wagenburg,* a ring of covered wagons, as the backbone of their defense; from these their halberdiers sallied out. About half of the Hussites were crossbowmen and handgunners; when reloading, they took cover behind *pavises,* large shields set on the ground. After the original cause of their rebellion had died down, many of them had become professional soldiers and served as mercenaries all over Europe. Citizen-soldiers of many free cities were quick to adopt this way of fighting, which combined maneuverability with safety.

DURER, *Five Warriors*

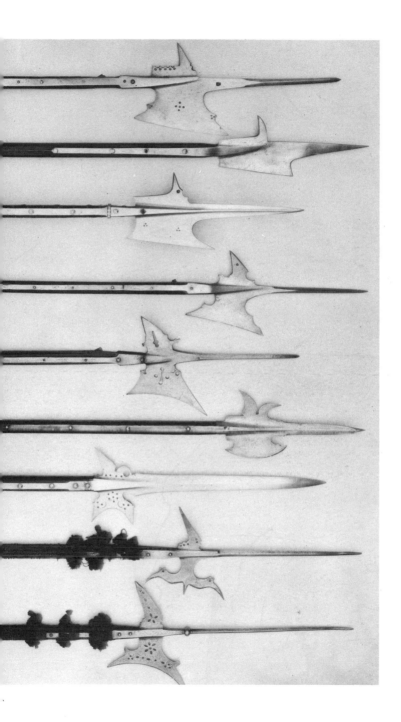

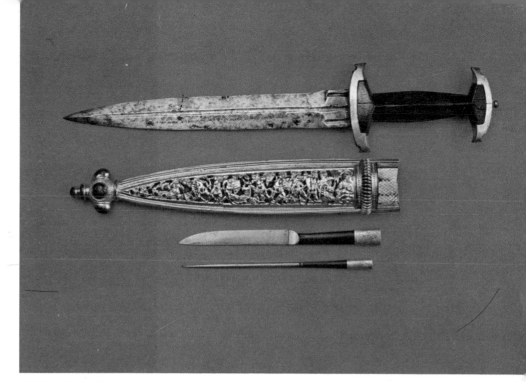

SWISS DAGGER AND SHEATH

In the second half of the fifteenth century the Swiss soldiers became the models for regular infantry on the continent. French and Italian princes hired Swiss pikemen as mercenaries—there is a Swiss guard at the Vatican even today—and Emperor Maximilian patterned the German *landsknechte* after them. Their weapons included crossbows that were too strong to be spanned by hand; in most cases a device like an autojack was used. Their halberds were perhaps the most versatile shafted weapon ever designed; they had an axelike blade for hacking, a spike for stabbing, and in back a hook suited for grappling or pulling down a horsemen. For fighting at close quarters short swords were used; the Swiss sported a special type of dagger elaborately decorated. Officers carried particularly fine specimens as badges of rank, many of them designed by famous artists, like Hans Holbein, who later went to England to become court painter to Henry VIII.

COSTUME ARMOR

Suits of armor were sometimes actually built to resemble suits of clothes.

The German *landsknechte,* foot soldiers of the early sixteenth century, wore no uniforms but strove to outdo each other in the extravagancies of their swashbuckling costumes. The basic features of their dress were puffed sleeves and tight hose; bold slashes supposed to simulate sword cuts were used as fancy decorative elements. The lining showing through the slashes was usually of a different color, and heightened the gaudy effect of the whole.

Soon it became fashionable for knights to captain these soldiers and some of them went so far as to order armor made to imitate the *landsknechte* dress. It was a great challenge for the armorer to recreate wide sleeves out of interlocking and telescoping elements, and to copy with embossing, etching, gilding and other skillful surface treatments the slashes of different colors, or the texture of rich fabrics.

Noblemen who preferred a more dignified appearance copied in steel the wide-skirted coats worn at court. These steel coats had cutouts for horseback riding; when the owner was on foot the cutouts could be closed with extra pieces that fit into the gaps. Even small pieces of equipment like daggers often reflected the puffs and slashes of fashionable clothes.

PRE-COLUMBIAN AMERICA

In 1519 Cortez set out and conquered Mexico; twelve years later Pizarro overthrew Peru. Cortez wrote in one of his reports that everything he saw was so strange that he sometimes wondered if he had landed on the moon.

Very few pieces of ancient-American weaponry have come down to us, but we know the appearance of Mexican and Peruvian warriors quite well from their works of art. In Peru the early civilization of the Mochica (300 B.C.-700 A.D.) produced many figure vessels. On them we find warriors splendidly attired in thickly quilted cotton jackets, padded helmets, and stout shields. Each is armed with a club and a pair of javelins. The war club had a stone head and on its other end a wicked spike of copper, to be used like rifle butt and bayonet; the javelins were hurled with a special device, a spear-thrower, that gave additional leverage to the warriors' arm. Apparently there were two groups or clans of warriors, identified by animal badges, the Foxes and the Hawks. The armies of the Inca were attired and armed in a very similar way.

LIP PLUG

In Mexico the Aztecs based their entire society on warfare, partly to extort tribute, and partly to capture victims for sacrifices to their bloodthirsty gods. They even had a standing arrangement with a neighboring tribe, the Tlaxcaltecs, to fight ceremonial battles for the sole purpose of taking prisoners for sacrifice. Defensive armor was of cotton quilt: a sleeveless jacket for the common warrior and an overall garment for the higher ranks. Since the eagle and the jaguar were symbols of courage, the quilt armor of the two highest classes of warrior were covered with eagle feathers or jaguar skin, and their helmets were in the shape of the animals' heads.

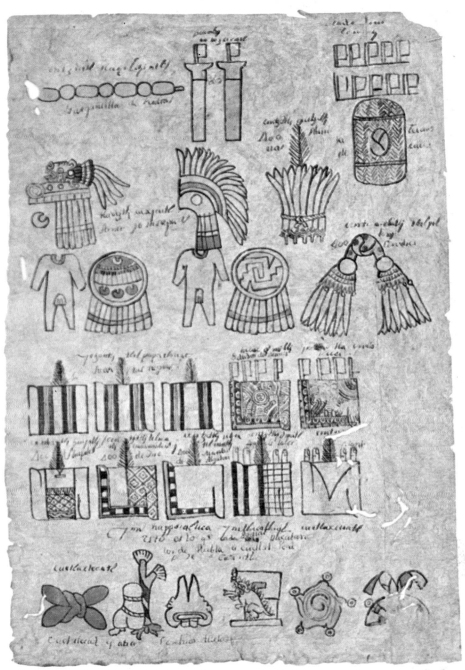

COPY OF A TRIBUTE ROLL SHOWING ARMOR

The Aztec army was very well organized. Each rank was distinguished by a special headdress and shield emblem; and the fighting units each had a specific banner, worn tied to the unit leader's back. The smallest unit to have a banner of its own was a group of twenty warriors, so the hieroglyph for twenty in Aztec pictorial writing is a little banner.

Weapons were a swordlike club with saw-toothed edges of obsidian, and a javelin designed to be thrown with a spear-thrower. The javelins were usually carried in bundles of four. Shield, war club, and spear bundle combined were the hieroglyph for "campaign, battle".

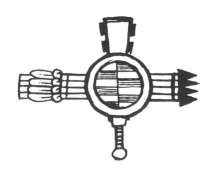

AZTEC SYMBOL FOR BATTLE

THE CONQUISTADORS

Although there were numerous pikemen, crossbowmen, and handgunners in Spain, the real strength of Spanish infantry lay with its swordsmen. The adventurers who sailed to America were, more often than not, poor noblemen who owned little more than sword and buckler. The swords were forged in Toledo, one of the most famous centers of this art, and the bucklers were usually *adargas,* oval shields adopted from the Moors. The adargas were of stiff leather and therefore rather light, but tough. When the conquistadors came to Mexico they found that the quilt armor of the Aztecs was much better suited to local conditions than steel armor; for not only did the steel armor get intolerably hot in the sun, but the obsidian-tipped weapons of the Aztecs broke into a shower of glass-sharp splinters when they hit steel. Soon the Spanish wore quilt armor too. On the other hand their iron swords, their cannon, and above all their horses proved to be far superior to anything their opponents could muster. Spanish horses had long been considered to be the best chargers a knight could own. They were strong enough to carry an armored man, and were still swift of foot. The famous white horses of the Spanish riding school in Vienna are direct descendants of these old battle chargers.

69

TOURNAMENTS

A knight's duty was fighting, but in peacetime he could show his prowess in a tournament. Originally—in the thirteenth century—the knight rode into the lists armed as if he were going to battle; but gradually special reinforcement pieces were developed for tournament use that were too heavy and encumbering for the field. Finally—around 1500—tournament armor had become quite different from field armor. About a dozen types of tournament armor were known, differentiated mostly by the helmets used. These were all derivations of the three basic types: the old pot helm, now solidly screwed to the breast and backplate; the sallet, with a chin defense extending over breast and shoulder; and the visored armet reinforced with chin and neckguards.

IVORY CASKET LID
SHOWING TOURNAMENT

TILTING ARMOR

70

From the beginning tournaments were grand spectacles accompanied by pageants, like the Siege of the Castle of Love, where flowers were used instead of arrows and sling-stones. The more elaborate the tournament became, the less it resembled a real battle. The most famous form of the tournament was the joust, where the knights tried to unhorse each other with lances. This could be one man against another, or as *mêlée,* in which two groups attacked each other. Other tournaments were fought with blunt swords, either on horseback, when the aim was to knock off the opponent's crest, or on foot, when each combatant had to strike a certain number of blows in turn. Only when the jousters were charging alongside a barrier did they wear leg armor as protection from accidental bumps; otherwise they discarded it, for it was against the rules to hit below the belt. In spite of this, the total weight of tournament armor could be over one hundred pounds because of the extreme thickness of the metal. However, it was worn only for a relatively short time.

TOURNAMENT, FOOT COMBAT

FOOT COMBAT ARMOR

effect. This was the method of the German armorers; the Italians preferred to cover the entire surface with the acid-resistant coating and scratch the design into the coating with the point of a needle before applying the acid.

ETCHED ARMOR OF THE MID-XVI CENTURY

Plate armor was designed to present a glancing surface to the point of a weapon. If it was to be decorated and still be practical, it had to keep the deflecting quality of the smooth plates and a uniform thickness of metal. The armorers therefore decorated by etching. The design was painted on with a mixture of liquid wax and resin, then acid was poured on to eat into the surface at the uncovered spots. When the coating was removed, the design stood out brightly against the dark areas where the acid has had its

The etching technique probably originated from the custom of rustproofing armor by painting it black. (Remember that the "Black Knight" in the stories is always a loner? He could do without a squire because his armor did not have to be polished). When a repaint job became necessary, one observant armorer probably noticed that scratches in the paint showed up as lines in the metal, and he might have thought of using this effect for decorative purposes. Soon artists discovered that an etched plate produced finer details in printing than a woodcut; and armorers in their turn used artists' prints as models for their designs.

DETAIL OF BREASTPLATE

ETCHED GARNITURES

Armor was always expensive (even the unpretentious mail shirt of the early Middle Ages was worth the equivalent of ten cows), and those who could afford it, tried to make the most of it. Since there were separate types of armor for field and tournament, it became fashionable to have matching, exchangable outfits. The armorers of Augsburg were the first to develop an ingenious system of suits of armor equipped with exchange pieces that could be combined to form units for all occasions. Some of the more extensive garnitures of this kind consisted of more than two hundred single elements, including matching horse armor and saddles. The armor of the Earl of Cumberland illustrated here has four spare vamplates for lances.

ARMOR OF
THE EARL OF PEMBROKE

ELBOW
GUARD

ARMOR OF
THE EARL OF CUMBERLAND

74

Besides heavy reinforcement elements for the tournament, a garniture usually had special light pieces, too, that could be worn with greater comfort in the field; items such as open-faced burgonets or "animes": flexible breastplates built up from overlapping hoops.

Besides the workshops of Augsburg, those at Landshut in Bavaria, Milan, and the Royal English workshop in Greenwich (staffed with German workmen) excelled in fine and rich garnitures.

SMYTHE
SHIELD

ARMOR OF
CONNETABLE MONTMORENCY

ARMOR OF
GRAND MASTER OF ARTILLERY GENOUILHAC

75

EMBOSSED PARADE ARMOR

The manufacture of armor is actually sculpture in steel, and the armorers often tried to prove their skill by creating extravagant designs. The German masters especially loved to devise grotesque faces that made helmets more weird looking, and took particular pride in shaping raised elements like a mustache or a rooster's wattles from the solid piece.

76

These helmets could be used for combat, but most of the fancy decorative armor was purely for parade purposes. Because of its great expense, armor was always a status symbol, like jewelry; and in parade armor it became the most extensive jewelry ever designed, covering its wearer literally from top to toe.

SHIELD OF HENRY II

ARMOR OF THE DUKE OF ALBA

77

There were masters who specialized in this work: in Milan, and especially in the court workshop of King Henry II of France. The most elaborate pieces of armor displayed entire scenes from classical history and mythology. It is tragic that King Henry II, who owned the most magnificent suits of armor, was killed in a tournament accident.

Embossing was done by hammering out the rough contours of the pattern from the backside; then the fine details were chiseled in from the outside. The hammering was done on a soft surface, like a block of lead or a bowl filled with pitch.

ARMOR OF
HENRY II

An essential part of the appearance of the armor in a parade were the trimmings of plumes and fabrics; these are shown on the riders in armor *alla romana* from a hand-painted book commemorating tournaments and pageants held in the city of Nürnberg during the fifteenth and sixteenth centuries. Such elaborate armor, with its plates freely embossed in relief, no longer presented the smooth glancing surface against a lance, that had been the original purpose of plate armor.

CRUCIFORM SWORD

SWORD WITH
SINGLE FINGER GUARD

SWORD WITH
KNUCKLEGUARD

REITSCHWERT

SWEPT HILT RAPIER

DEVELOPMENT OF THE SWORD

The medieval sword was cruciform in shape with plain quillons for stopping the opponent's weapon, and a heavy pommel counterbalancing the blade. It was held in the clenched fist, which was protected by a gauntlet. In a stabbing thrust, the knight achieved a firmer grip by hooking his index finger around the quillon, but in a parry this finger was in grave danger of being sliced off; so a loop for its protection was added. Later, as fencing styles became more elaborate, the steel gauntlet was discarded as a hindrance to the free movement of the wrist. More and more branches were added to the guard for the protection of the hand, until the full swept hilt was developed in the late sixteenth century.

The early seventeenth century brought the cuphilted rapier, ideally suited to the purely thrusting technique of the Spanish fencing school; it was used with a matching dagger for the left hand to parry and catch the opponent's blade. In the Rococo period the rapier degenerated into the dainty court sword with a hilt of silver, enamel or even porcelain. Special weapons were the swords for two hands: the Scottish *claymore,* for example, or the *Bidenhander* wielded by picked *landsknechte* troops. Military swords designed for cutting blows were either curved sabers or heavy single-edged blades like the basket-hilted broadsword.

Famous sword-making centers were Toledo in Spain, Passau on the Danube, Solingen in the Rhineland, and — of course — Milan.

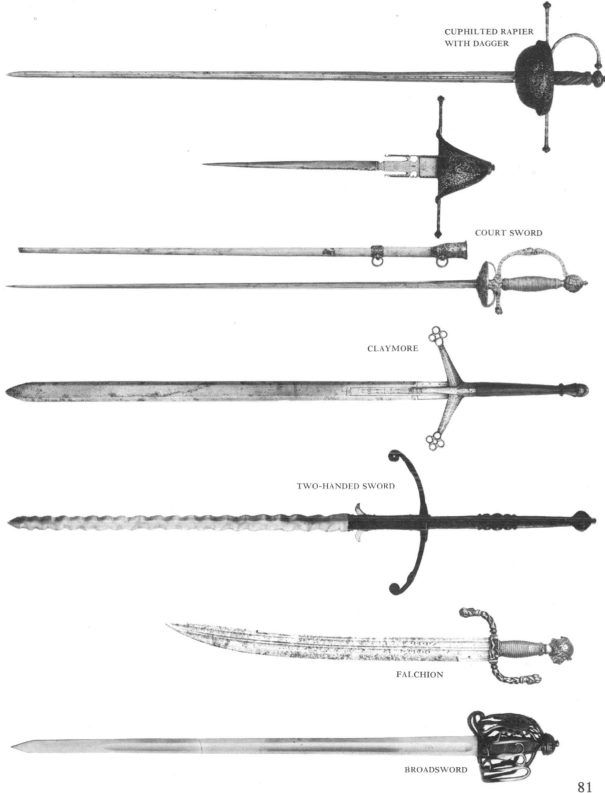

CUPHILTED RAPIER
WITH DAGGER

COURT SWORD

CLAYMORE

TWO-HANDED SWORD

FALCHION

BROADSWORD

81

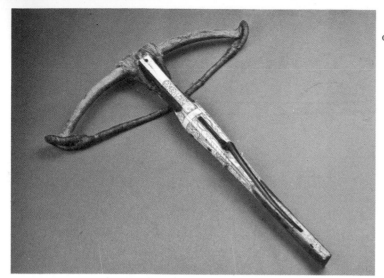

CROSSBOW

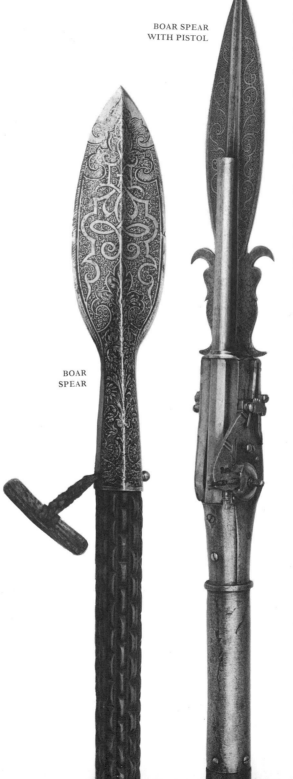

BOAR SPEAR

BOAR SPEAR WITH PISTOL

BOAR SPEAR

HUNTING WEAPONS

Hunting for meat was a necessity, but the danger and excitement of it also made it the most important sport. Even after the introduction of guns, the silent crossbow was considered to be the proper weapon for almost all kinds of hunting. Spears were also used. These had a toggle behind the head to prevent the animal from running up too close.

For those who wanted to be even more sporting, special swords were designed for the boar hunt; and here armor was worn by the hunter and by his favorite dogs as a protection against the terrible tusks of the boar. Hunting swords were for the *coup-de-grâce* when the quarry was brought down; broad-bladed hunting knives served to cut up the carcass.

HUNTING SWORD

HUNTING SWORD
WITH **PISTOL**

HUNTING KNIFE

BOAR SWORD

83

DEVELOPMENT OF FIREARMS

Guns were already in use in the middle of the fourteenth century; but these "handcannons" were crude affairs, better suited to scaring the horses of charging knights than scoring hits. They were ignited by a burning match—a wick impregnated with saltpeter and spirit of wine—held to the touch hole. Since it was impossible to aim the gun and apply the match by hand, a mechanical ignition device was constructed. This matchlock had an arm where the match could be secured by a screw. The match was moved against the pan holding the priming powder by pulling a long trigger similar to the ones on crossbows. Some matchlock guns had a hook under the barrel to take up the recoil when they were fired from a parapet; these "hook-guns" were called *Hakenbüchse* in German, and from this word derived *hackbut* and *arquebuse.* Another heavy gun, originally set on a fork, was the *musket;* its name comes from the Spanish *mosquito,* because of the irritating effect the flanking gunners had on squares of pikemen.

Lighted matches and gunpowder were a dangerous combination, so gunsmiths worked on self-igniting devices. The first one, invented in Germany in the early sixteenth century, was the wheellock. It worked like a cigarette lighter, striking sparks from a stone held against a spring-driven steel wheel; the wheel was wound up with a special spanner.

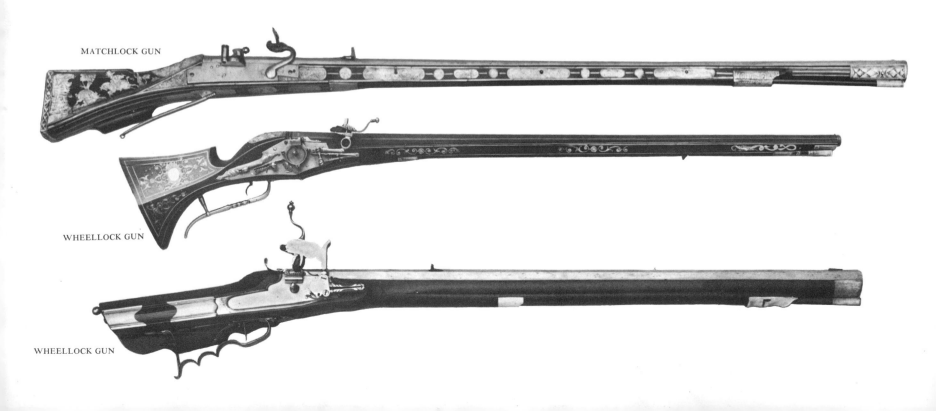

MATCHLOCK GUN

WHEELLOCK GUN

WHEELLOCK GUN

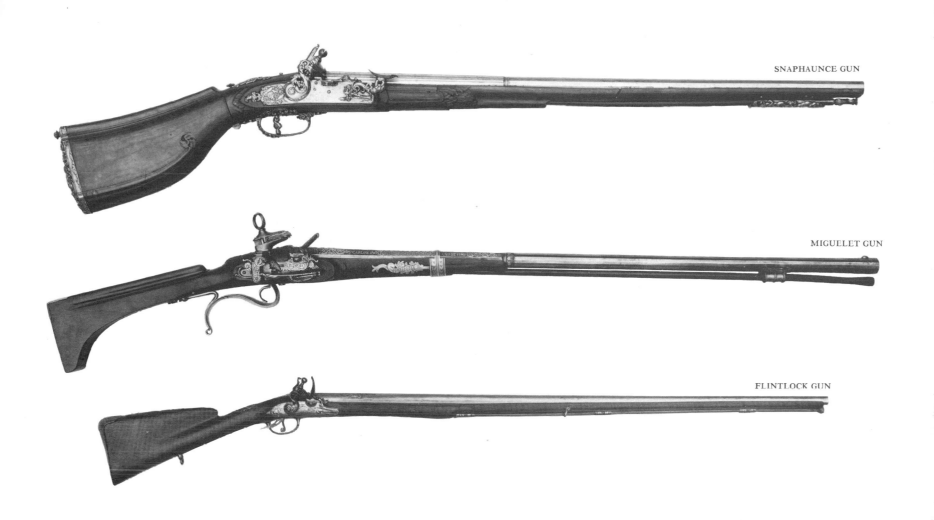

SNAPHAUNCE GUN

MIGUELET GUN

FLINTLOCK GUN

Though reliable, the wheellock was complicated and difficult to repair when broken. Soon other systems were developed, one where a hammer holding a flintstone was snapped against a steel plate on top of the pan was known as the "Dutch" lock and was called *snaphaunce,* which means "pecking rooster". A simplified version was the "Spanish" lock or *miquelet,* named after a band of Spanish highwaymen. The simplest and most efficient was the "French" flint lock. Invented by Master Marin le Bourgeoys in the small town of Lisieux, around 1615, it dominated all battlefields and hunting grounds in Europe and America well into the nineteenth century.

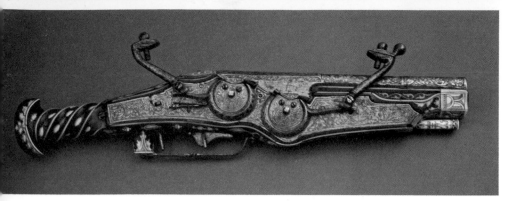

DOUBLE-BARRELED PISTOL

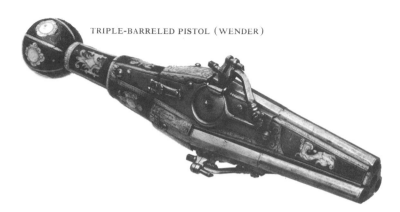

TRIPLE-BARRELED PISTOL (WENDER)

MULTISHOTS AND BREECHLOADERS

Most early guns loaded their shot through the muzzle. The difficulty of reloading made it desirable to have a second or even a third shot ready when the first had missed its mark. The problem was solved by joining two or more barrels and locks together; for a second shot, the gun was spun around. More tricky was the method of loading two charges in the same barrel, one on top of the other, to be ignited by two locks, one in front of the other. Breech-loading was tried as early as the fifteenth century for ships' cannon, where it was impossible to get in front of the barrel to reload, but it could not be very successful as long as the ignition depended on a touch hole.

DOUBLE-BARRELED PISTOL (WENDER)

BREECH-LOADING CANNON

DOUBLE-SHOT CARBINE (ROMAN CANDLE)

86

CABASSET

ARMOR IN THE XVII CENTURY

Reformation and Counter-Reformation resulted in a series of wars in Northern Europe, among them the War of the Gueuses, the Thirty Years' War, and the English Civil War. During these conflicts the importance of firearms grew steadily and armor grew less useful; in order to stop a bullet from a musket it had to be so thick it was too heavy for comfort. Those cavalry troops that carried long guns, like the dragoons or the French Horse Musketeers, did not wear armor any more. On the other hand, armor was still quite useful for the heavy cavalry armed with a brace of saddle pistols and a sword. The Pappenheim black cuirassiers and Cromwell's Ironsides were armored with breast- and back-plate, arm defenses, and leg armor, but only down to the knee.

VELASQUEZ, *Duke of Olivares*

THREE-QUARTER ARMOR

Their helmets were mostly open-faced, with a "lobster-tail" neckguard, because the field of vision was too much obstructed by a closed visor to allow the handling of pistols. Standard equipment for light troops was a thick buff coat and a broad-brimmed felt hat, usually worn with a steel skull cap underneath. Sometimes a cavalier's entire hat was constructed of steel.

English pikemen were the last to wear armor—cuirass with wide tassets, wide-brimmed helmet, and elbow-length gauntlets. This armor came to Colonial America, where it proved to be quite effective against Indian arrows.

MUSKETEER

PIKEMAN'S ARMOR

THE SUN KING

Until the second half of the seventeenth century armies consisted of mercenaries hired only for the campaign at hand. The units were disbanded at the end of the war. Louis XIV, King of France, was the first to set up a standing army of regular regiments, clad in regular uniforms. (Before that time every soldier wore his own clothes, and friend and foe were distinguished only by the colors of hat plumes or sashes.) At this time the introduction of the bayonet made both musketeer and pikeman of every infantryman; afterward only officers carried polearms; sergeants halberds, and commissioned officers partisans. Armor shrank to breast- and backplate for cuirassiers; full armor was worn only by the highest ranks out of a sense of knightly tradition (especially when posing for an impressive portrait), rather than for actual protection.

RIGAUD, *Portrait of Maréchal La Tour*

THE TURKS

At about the time of the Crusades a formidable military power emerged right at Europe's southern border, the Turks. Originally one of those steppe nomad tribes like the Huns, they had swept into the Near East, sabred away at the Byzantine Empire until its final overthrow, and then started a chain of conquest that netted them the Eastern half of the Mediterranean, and brought them twice to the very gates of Vienna.

The Turks were dashing horsemen above all, plying powerful reflex bows and flashing scimitars. They wore mail or *jazerant* (mail reinforced with small steel plates) together with tall conical helmets and elbow-length arm guards.

SCIMITAR OF MURAD V

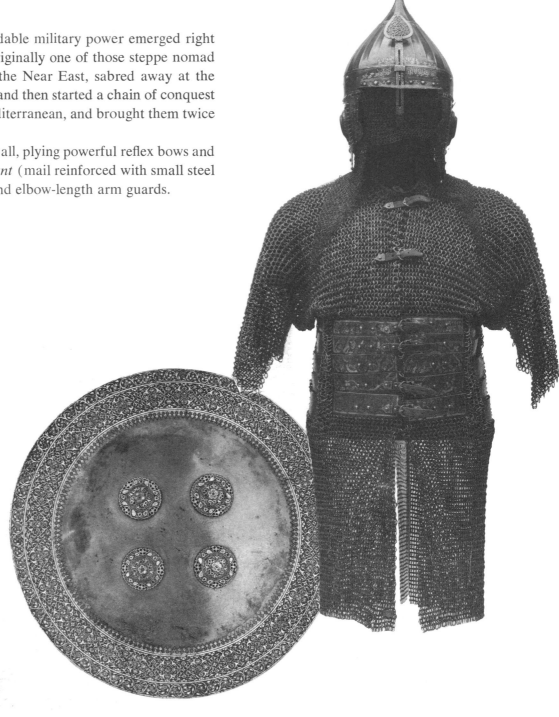

TURKISH HELMET

Later pistols replaced the bow; these were not worn in saddleholsters as was European custom, but thrust through the sash, preferably with a couple of matching daggers.

Besides their renowned cavalry, the Turks had a famous corps of infantry, the Jenissaries. These men were levied as boys from the large non-Moslem population within the Turkish Empire and given fanatical training. Their organization in many respects was much better than that of the Western European armies; instead of living by plundering the countryside, they had a well-ordered supply system and community-cooking. (Jenissary officers had titles like "meat-cutter" or "soup-distributor", and they wore spoons in silver cases as regimental badges on their white felt caps). Turkish regimental brass bands were enthusiastically imitated in the West, replacing the fife and drum of the *landsknechte* days.

TURKISH MINIATURE,
ARMY ENTERING CITY

HELMET

PERSIAN MINIATURE, BATTLE SCENE

PERSIA

Fine workmanship has always distinguished Persian products, and especially their weapons. Not only were the best mail and finest helmets of the Islamic world made in Persia, but also the most celebrated swords of pattern-welded steel. They became known as "Damascus blades" in Europe, after the place from which they were exported, but actually they were manufactured in Persia. Even the word "scimitar" is derived from the Persian *shamshir,* "lion's tail" (because the sweeping curve of the blade resembles the tail of a lion).

OXHEAD MACE

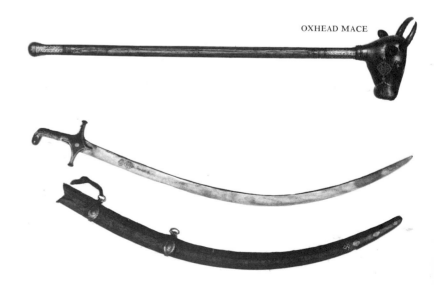

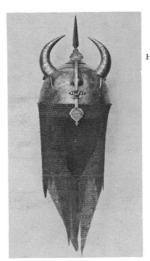

HORNED HELMET

INDIA

Indian weapons began to show a Persian influence after invasions into India from the West in the sixteenth century, though Indian traditions were strong enough to affect the results. The *shamshir* blade was fitted with the mushroom-shaped Indian sword hilt to form the *tulwar,* and Persian helmets received decorative attachments that suited the more fantastic Indian taste.

A typical Indian practice, of course, was the use of war elephants. They were used against Alexander the Great, and as years went by they were gradually adapted to changing weapons and warfare, as can be seen from this chess piece of an elephant carrying a cannon at each side of his howdah.

AXE

TULWAR

Indian firearms were usually long guns. They are often extravagantly decorated and shaped (the Metropolitan Museum has one with a square bore.). Almost all of them were matchlocks.

The strangest-looking Indian weapons are the *khattar* dagger and the gauntlet sword. The fist had to grasp a cross-bar handle on the dagger, and use the blade in a punching thrust. The gauntlet sword fitted over hand and forearm; the enforced inflexibility of the wrist must have made any fencing beyond flailing blows impracticable.

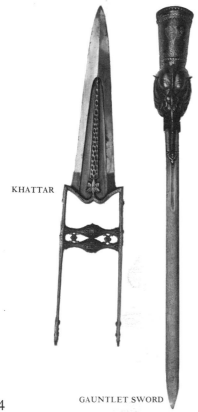

KHATTAR

GAUNTLET SWORD

94

KRISSTAND

INDONESIA

Though it consists of thousands of islands, hundreds of tribes, and dozens of languages, Indonesia has one universal weapon—the *kris,* a strangely asymmetrical dagger. Its blade can be straight or wavy, depending on whether it is supposed to symbolize a sleeping or a running serpent; it should be made of seven different metals, a process that definitely does not produce superior steel, but increases the blade's magical virtues. Magic was also a part of the small carved figure of a demon that formed the grip; it was he who gave the weapon its power to kill.

Besides the *kris* the Indonesians had all sorts of swords and spears, some of them in the most bizarre shapes ever invented. Among the missile weapons the most famous is the blowpipe with its poisoned darts.

On most of the islands no armor was worn, though some warriors had helmets or cuirasses after Indian. Chinese, or even European prototypes. Particularly impressive are the brass versions of the burgonets and morions worn by Portuguese and Spanish explorers of the sixteenth century, made by the Moros of the Philippines. The choice of material for cuirasses was often highly original too, including water buffalo horn, crocodile skin and scales of the pangolin.

BRASS HELMET

MORO ARMOR

96

CHINA

The Chinese did most of their fighting against foreign invaders. As wave after wave of nomad warriors swarmed out of the Mongolian steppes, the Chinese adopted arms and armor from their enemies. Their curved sabres, for example, with two carrying clasps on the scabbards, are related to those of the Turks and even of the Huns, who originally came from the Central Asian steppes. On the other hand, the Chinese never gave up their traditional straight sword, and they clung to their crossbow. They even invented a repeating system of firing the crossbows to keep up with the fast shooting nomad bows.

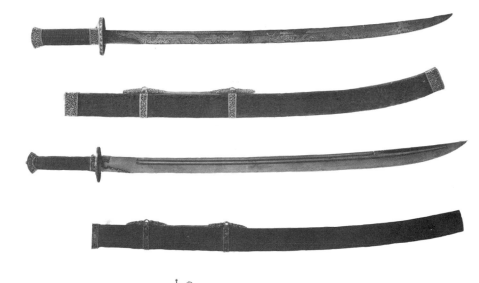

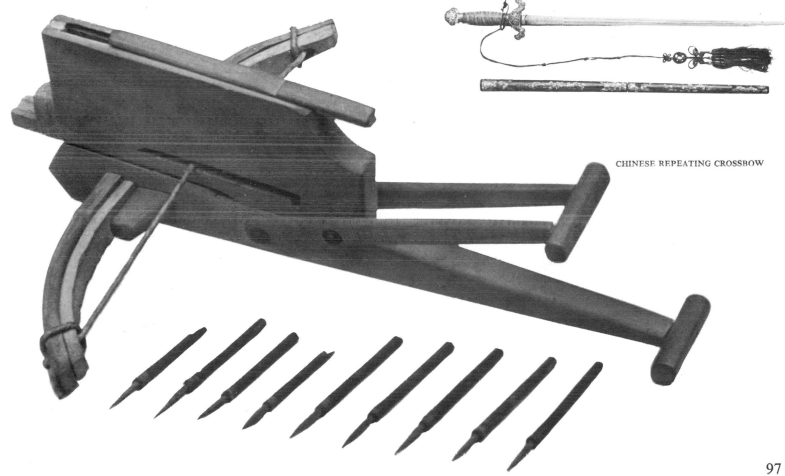

CHINESE REPEATING CROSSBOW

Body armor consisted of jackets and skirts with iron scales riveted in as a lining; the rivets showed on the outside, and were used as a decorative element. Helmets were of the typical Asian form with cheekpieces, hanging neck guards, and high, impressive crests.

There were attempts made to increase the range of arrows by tying rockets to them. But otherwise, gunpowder—though it was known to the Chinese centuries before the European heard of it— was not used in warfare, supposedly for humanitarian reasons. (In Europe the Pope declared a ban on the use of crossbows except against infidels in 1138, but evidently none of the good Christians cared.)

JAPAN

The Japanese samurai was, in spirit, very much like the medieval knight, though his armor was developed on an entirely different principle. While European armor was solid to break the shock of a blow by its rigidity, the samurai's armor of steel scales and silk braid was flexibly laced together. It was designed to give under a blow and absorb the shock—or, even better, to permit the warrior to dodge a sword stroke altogether by nimble footwork.

The armor was meticulously built up of thousands of scales, lacquered against rust, and of silk braid in distinctive colors that announced the wearer's rank. Particularly conspicuous were the *sode*, large boxlike shoulder- and armguards, designed to catch arrows and blades before they came too close. Helmet bowls were composed of many small precisely shaped steel plates; each helmet had a small hole on top, not only for ventilation, but also to permit the fighting spirit of the war god to enter the body of the warrior in battle. Bold crests were worn at the front of the helmet for identification. Fierce steel masks were tied over the face to frighten the enemy as well as to protect the wearer against sword cuts.

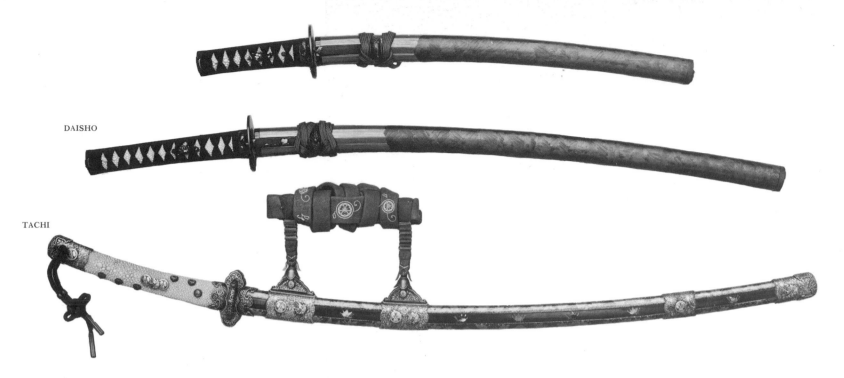

DAISHO

TACHI

KNIFE HANDLES

The Japanese sword and its uses is a science in itself. The sword was considered to be the "soul of the samurai." Japanese blades are the finest ever made: hammered, honed, and polished with infinite patience and skill for months by masters working in century-old traditions. Japanese sword mountings are among the most refined metalwork ever done anywhere. It was the privilege of a samurai to carry two swords tucked at his side: a long *katana* and a short *wakizashi;* as a pair they were called *daisho*. With armor or certain ceremonial robes a *tachi* or slung sword might be worn.

100

SWORD GUARD

Archery was as important as swords-manship. The Japanese bow is one of the longest ever made. Its unique feature is that it is not grasped in the center, but well below it; therefore the two arms of the bow must be of different flexibility, but of equal strength.

In the year 1542 a new weapon, the gun, was introduced into Japan through Portuguese explorers. Within twenty years muskets were carried by ten thousand Japanese soldiers, and were especially favored by the two greatest generals of the period, Nobunaga and Hideyoshi. Nobunaga even wrote a military manual on the art of shooting. The woodcut reproduced here is a picture from his book.

CEREMONIAL ARROWHEADS

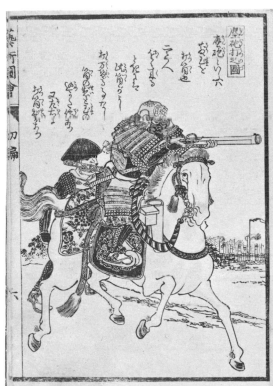

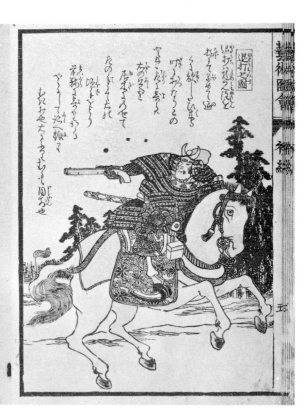

With warlike virtues held in such high esteem in old Japan, it is not surprising that innumerable works of art—scroll paintings, folding screens, and prints—show military scenes. Yet they were not all serious. The battle themes could be seen with a satirical eye, as in this print of a titanic struggle between an army of cats and, an army of mice, fighting it out with all the typical fencing postures of the true samurai.

XVIII CENTURY EUROPE

However deadly its battles were, it is said of the eighteenth century that it fought "La guerre en dentelles"—a lace-trimmed war. The French cuirassier captain here in his freshly powdered wig, with a fine film of powder on the shoulder of his red velvet coat (as carefully recorded by the painter), is ready for action, though to us it looks more as if he were going on parade. By now the cuirassiers were the only troops that still wore armor, but reduced to breast- and backplates; some armies had done away even with the backplate as unnecessary, since a good soldier was not supposed to turn his back anyway.

FLINTLOCK
PISTOLS

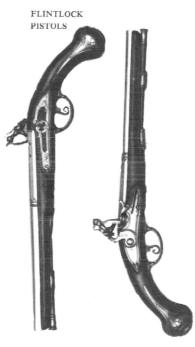

XVIII CENTURY AMERICA

In the New World things were different. Although British and colonial regulars were trained to handle their muskets in the established military style of volley and bayonet charge, with no thought of bodily protection, the militia volunteers had learned from the Indian that a tree trunk would make a stouter shield than most. Another thing inspired by the Indian, in this case his feather of honor for "counting coup," was the awarding of military decorations for personal valor, like the medal Major Willett is wearing here.

XVIII CENTURY

For an army fighting with flintlock muskets, strict fire discipline and precision in maneuvers were absolutely necessary. The Prussian infantryman, unequalled, was drilled into firing five shots a minute, which meant a rolling charge with volleys three seconds apart from a line four deep. These soldiers were conscripts, often even pressed into service, and held there only by the most rigorous discipline. Enterprising princes lent or even sold their troops to whoever might need them. (The Landgrave of Hesse, in typical eighteenth century sophistication, used the money he received for his cannon fodder, the unfortunate Hessians, to buy some new Rembrandts for this painting collection.)

Infantry officers wore gorgets as badges of rank; these were the last remnants, now purely ornamental, of the old breastplates.

Cavalry, who fought more with the sword than did the infantry, still liked to have a solid protection for the head, and therefore wore helmets of brass or hard leather long after the rest of the army had abandoned any kind of armor. There were no cuirassiers with breastplates in the United States, but the Mexican *dragons de la cuera* wore buff coats and even *adargas* in battles with the Indians up to the early nineteenth century.

Though many European armies had rifle companies, the fame of the American rifleman overshadowed them all. The famous "Kentucky" rifles were actually made in Pennsylvania (the word "rifle" is derived from the German *riffeln*—to make small grooves), and suited the conditions of the American frontier marvelously.

THE NAPOLEONIC PERIOD

After the American and the French Revolutions, the status of the common soldier was considerably improved; and proud citizens fought where earlier men had been pressed into service. The new-found pride of the fighting man was shown in uniforms that were designed more and more to be attractive. During the time of France's greatest military genius, Napoleon, the splendor of uniforms was unsurpassed. Armor was still worn by the French cuirassiers, and they found that in the Russian campaign their opponents included hordes of tribal warriors from the southern steppes and the Caucasus, some of whom still wore Persian mail shirts and shields.

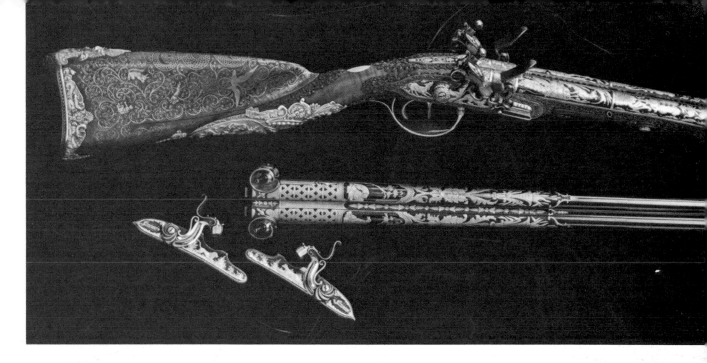

Besides mass-produced weapons for the ever-demanding armies, very fine decorative arms for presentation purposes were designed, often — as was the case with Nicholas Noel Boutet in Versailles — by the same men who turned out flintlock muskets and saddle pistols by the thousands.

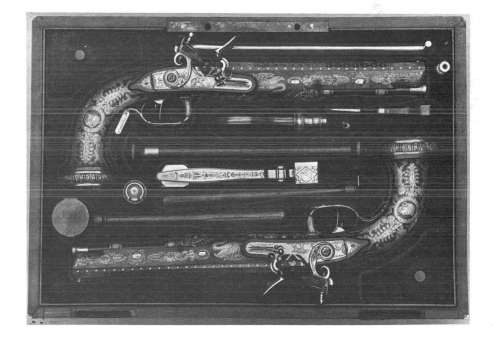

107

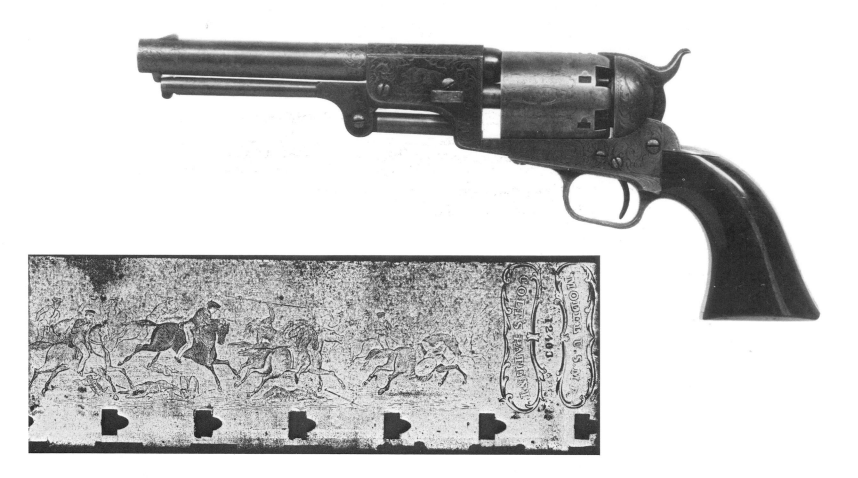

XIX CENTURY AMERICA

The main weapon in any Western is the smoking colt. Most people use the brand name "Colt" as another word for "revolver"; and Samuel Colt himself did his best to convince the world that the revolver was his own invention, though revolving chambered cylinders had been in use since the sixteenth century. Colt's model, however, was the first workable one that could be mass-produced. It proved its value in the famous Texas Ranger fight against the Comanches. A picture of this episode was engraved on the cylinders of dragoon revolvers.

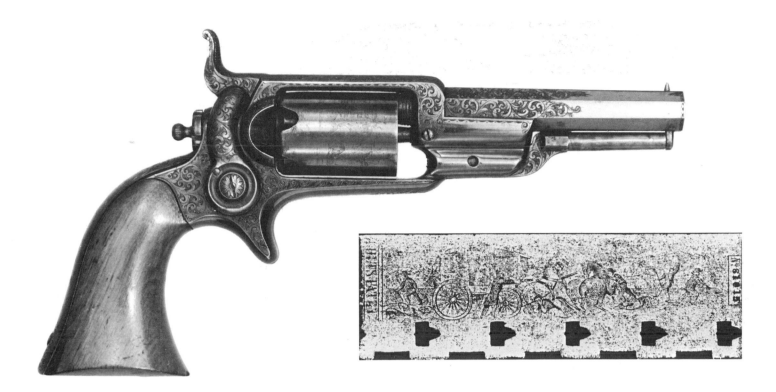

Navy colts and the five-shot model called the Wells-Fargo revolver had a naval battle and a stagecoach holdup as decoration.

Neither the US cavalry nor cowboys believed in armor; but their valiant foes, the Indians, did—though only in a limited way. They used buffalo-hide shields and breastplates of bone tubes strung together, both of which were good defenses against arrows and lances, and were even able to stop a halfspent bullet. Other protections, like the Ghost Dance shirts made bullet proof by magic, did not come up to expectations against the white man's stronger medicine.

XIX CENTURY
THE AGE OF THE
BREECH-LOADER

One of the drawbacks of firearms before the nineteenth century was that they had to be loaded through the muzzle. This made it difficult to get a gastight fit for the bullet and nearly impossible to reload in a prone position. Therefore gunsmiths long tried to find a way to load from the breech. But because the ignition depended on sparks struck outside the barrel and then flashing through the touchhole, no breech-loader was ever quite satisfactory. With the discovery of new explosive chemicals, fulminates, however, a cartridge containing bullet and explosive charge could be constructed. Consequently numerous kinds of breech-loaders appeared before the middle of the century. The first in Europe, and the most famous, was the Prussian needle gun, closely followed by the French *chassepot*. Through their successes in the Austrian and the Franco-Prussian wars, the Prussian army became once more a model to be copied. Even in America, where the French army was usually preferred as a model, versions of the Prussian spiked helmet were introduced.

During the Civil War American ingenuity produced a confusing multitude of breech-loading systems. Among them the Sharps rifle won lasting fame. Not only was the problem of loading at the breech now solved, but that of multi-shot arms, also; the Spencer carbine, and above all the Winchester—"the gun you load on Sunday and fire all week" —came to the fore; and if they did not decide the war, they won the West. These machine-produced weapons, however, were no works of the armorer's art. Though sporting arms and occasional presentation pieces were sometimes decorated with great skill, of military weapons nothing more was made that deserves a place in an art book.

111

ARMORED CARS AND ARMORED SHIPS

The newest developments in armor do deserve note. Most of them are concerned with protecting a whole fighting unit, such as the crew of a combat wagon or a warship. The charioteers of antiquity wore body armor, and so do the men on a cart in a military handbook of the fifteenth century; but it was also found desirable to encase the entire vehicle in a protective shell. A dragon-shaped war machine in the same handbook combines heavy armament with a frightful, if rather fanciful, appearance. The great problem for these projects was the lack of a power source that could be kept inside the protective armor. Draft horses were too exposed, and when they were incapacitated the whole was useless; ropes and pulleys managed from the inside were quite practical means of locomotion during a siege, but hopelessly inadequate in the open field.

Until recently ships were much better suited for carrying armor than carts. Already in the thirteenth century Chinese and Korean junks were covered with sheets of iron, and again the fifteenth century handbook shows an armored ship, definitely inspired by a medieval castle. In the following centuries attempts were repeatedly made to create ships as floating fortresses, but here the vulnerable sails could not possibly be protected. Only after the invention of the steam engine did there emerge the first true ironclads, the *Merrimac* and the *Monitor*. (The latter was the ancestor of all modern battleships, gun turret and all.) Later the invention of the combustion motor made possible the modern tank.

113

THE ARMORER'S WORKSHOP

Working in metal was a specialist's job from the beginning, and the making of good metal armor was something for a specialist within the profession. One of the earliest representations of an armorer is this small Greek bronze statuette. It was made at about the time Homer composed his epics about the heroes of the Trojan War, the eighth century B.C. This armorer is shaping the bowl of a helmet; unfortunately the handle of his hammer has corroded away and it is difficult to see that the projection on top of the helmet is the head of the hammer.

This woodcut of about 1515 by the German master Hans Burgkmair shows a visit of the Emperor Maximilian to his court workshop at Innsbruck. Maximilian "the Last of the Knights" was very much interested in all chivalrous pursuits, and the development and refinement of armor was one of his favorite concerns. The master armorer the emperor is talking to is probably Konrad Seusenhofer.

Though most of the work done today by the armorers in the Metropolitan Museum's workshop consists of cleaning and restoring the arms and armor in the Museum's collection, the men are still called upon to design armor when need arises. During both World Wars and the Korean War the Museum's armor shop was busy designing bullet-proof vests and steel helmets. One of these helmet models is shown at the left next to the boy's armor; this model was shaped by hand with tools that once served in the Armory of the Dukes of Saxony, in the ancient tradition of the days of chivalry.

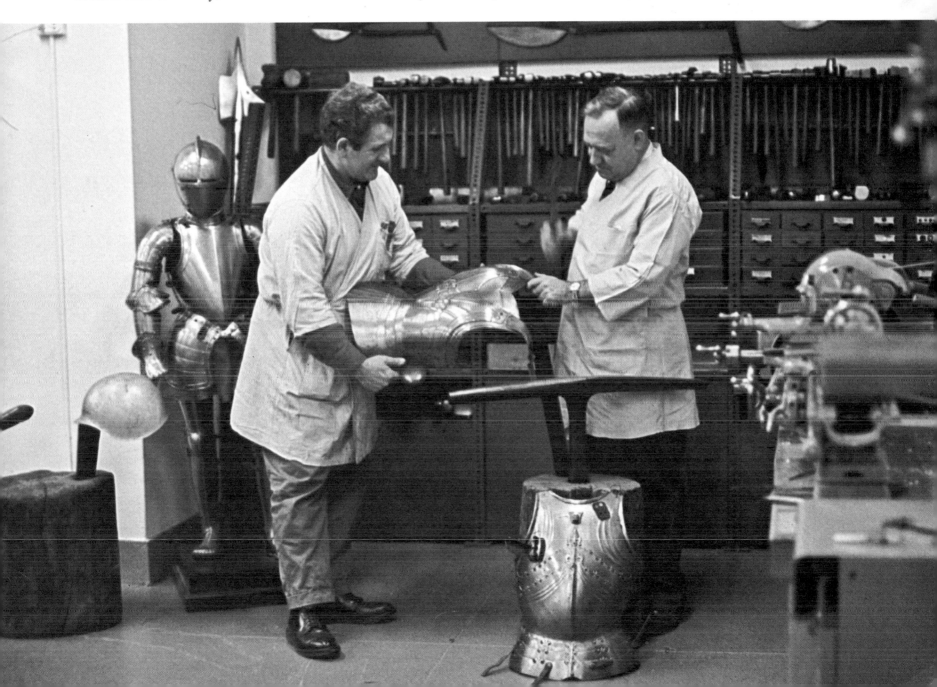

FIGURES OF SPEECH THAT HAVE SURVIVED FROM THE DAYS OF CHIVALRY

LOOKING FOR A CHINK IN SOMEONE'S ARMOR

UP IN ARMS

TO DIE IN HARNESS—"harness" originally meant a suit of armor.

TO BE CRESTFALLEN—in one kind of tournament the combattants tried to knock off each others' helmet crests with clubs or blunt swords. The winner was the one who kept his crest up to the last.

TO THROW DOWN THE GAUNTLET—throwing down a gauntlet in front of another knight was a challenge to combat; the challenge was accepted by picking up the gauntlet.

TO STRETCH A POINT—"points" were laces on a knight's doublet (the form-fitting jacket worn under the armor). These laces held parts of the arm and leg defenses in position; they had to be tied snugly, otherwise they might break under stress, and the armor become undone.

TO CARRY YOUR HEART ON YOUR SLEEVE—in a tournament a lady was expected to give a "favor" to her knight—a ribbon, a veil, etc—which he fastened to his left arm for all to see.

TO CROSS SWORDS WITH SOMEONE

TO PUMMEL SOMEONE—the pommel, the knob at the sword hilt, could be used in a backhanded blow at close quarters.

UP TO THE HILT

QUICK ON THE DRAW—this is older than the draw of the six-shooter; it comes from the drawing of the sword.

A STAB IN THE BACK

FREE LANCE—a "free lance" was a knight who did not own a castle, and therefore was free to fight for whoever hired him.

PLAIN AS A PIKESTAFF—the pike was the most ordinary of pole-arms, and therefore never decorated.

FULL TILT

TO DRAW A BEAD ON SOMEONE—the string of a longbow had a bead tied to its center at the place where the arrow was to be nocked; in "drawing the bead" the archer made ready to shoot.

SURVIVING FIGURES OF SPEECH DERIVED FROM THE USE OF ANCIENT FIREARMS

KEEP YOUR POWDER DRY—dryness of powder was absolutely essential for a muzzle-loading gun, because moist powder could not ignite from the sparks struck by the hammer.

ALL PRIMED UP—a pinch of priming powder was put into the pan in front of the touchhole; it was used to ignite the coarser powder of the charge in the barrel.

A FLASH IN THE PAN—sometimes only the priming powder went off, failing to ignite the charge.

NOT WORTH THE POWDER AND SHOT

LOCK, STOCK, AND BARREL

TO RAM IT HOME—in order to get enough gas pressure from the exploding powder charge it had to be packed tightly by ramming it in from the muzzle.

STRAIGHT AS A RAMROD—in order not to get stuck in the gun barrel the ramrod of a muzzle-loader had to be absolutely straight.

TO WORM SOMETHING OUT OF SOMEONE—if a charge was stuck in the barrel, it had to be drawn out by means of the "worm," a tool like a long corkscrew, that took hold in the soft lead bullet.

TO GO OFF HALF-COCKED—when the hammer of a flintlock was only pulled half the way back, it could be set at rest there, and safely carried when loaded. Unfortunately, if the moving parts of the lock were too much worn, the hammer might slip out of this "half-cock position," and accidentally ignite the powder charge.

TO SPIKE SOMEONE'S GUNS—cannon that had to be abandoned could be rendered useless to the enemy by hammering spikes or nails into the touchholes.

HOIST BY ONE'S OWN PETARD—a petard was a land mine to be attached to a gate in order to blow it up and breach it.

PARTING SHOT—this is a corruption of "Parthian Shot," named after the Parthians, an ancient Persian tribe. It was their custom in battle to pretend flight and then, turning around in the saddle, loose their arrows at their unwary pursuers.

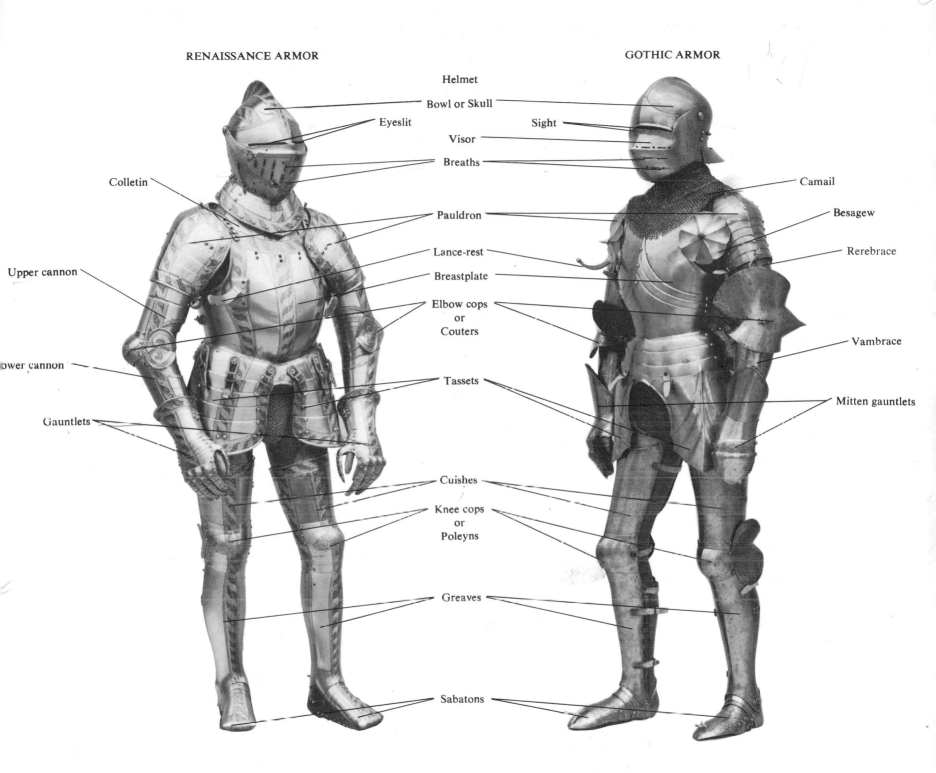

RENAISSANCE ARMOR

GOTHIC ARMOR

Helmet

Bowl or Skull

Eyeslit

Sight

Visor

Breaths

Colletin

Camail

Pauldron

Besagew

Lance-rest

Rerebrace

Breastplate

Elbow cops
or
Couters

Upper cannon

Vambrace

ower cannon

Tassets

Mitten gauntlets

Gauntlets

Cuishes

Knee cops
or
Poleyns

Greaves

Sabatons

117

GLOSSARY

ACCOLADE: the dubbing of a knight; from the Latin "collum"=neck, because the neck or shoulder of the young knight was given a light blow, often with the flat of a sword.

ACTON: the padded garment worn under a mail shirt; from the Spanish-Moorish "algoton"=cotton.

ADARGA: a light leather shield used by the Moors, but taken over by the Spaniards. The Indian-fighting Mexican *Dragons de la Cuera* (Leather Dragoons) used adargas until the early nineteenth century.

ALMAIN: the German armorers in the Royal English Armorers Shop in Greenwich; from the French "allemand"=German. Almain rivets are sliding rivets in slots, designed to give more flexibility to the armor elements.

ARMET: a close-fitting helmet with visor and movable cheekpieces.

ARQUEBUS: a light matchlock gun; from German "Hakenbüchse"= a gun with a hook (for taking the recoil when laid on a rampart).

BALDRIC: a shoulder belt for sword or hunting horn.

BALISTA: a throwing engine.

BANDOLEER: a musketeer's shoulder belt for holding cartridges.

BARD: the body armor of a knight's horse.

BASCINET: a light helmet of pointed form, with an attached neck-guard of mail.

BASILARD: a dagger with a hilt shaped like a letter I. The name derives from Basel, a town in Switzerland.

BASTON COURSE: a form of tournament fought on horseback with clubs or blunt swords; its object was to knock off the opponent's helmet crest.

BATTERING-RAM: a siege engine for breaking down walls or smashing a gate.

BEVOR: a chin-guard for an open helmet, such as a sallet.

BIDENHANDER: a two-handed sword; from German "with both hands."

BILL: a polearm for hacking; from German "Beil"= axe.

BOMBARD: an early cannon.

BRIGANDINE: a light body armor in form of a jacket lined with iron scales.

BUCKLER: a small fist shield for swordsmen.

BUFF COAT: a sleeveless jacket of thick leather (often buffalo leather, hence the name) worn as light body armor in the seventeenth century.

BYRNIE: a mail shirt of the early Middle Ages.

CABASSET: a light helmet; from Spanish "cabacete"=head piece.

CAMAIL: a mail neckguard.

CAPARISON: the ornamental coverings of a knight's horse.

CAP-A-PIE: fully armed; an old French term meaning "head to foot."

CATAPULT: a dart-throwing engine, already used by the Greeks and Romans.

CHANFRON: the head armor of a knight's horse.

CHAPEL-DE-FER: a broad-brimmed helmet; from French "hat of iron."

CHAUSSES: Early medieval leg armor of mail.

CLAYMORE: a two-handed Scottish sword; from Gaelic "cleagh mor" =big sword.

CONDOTTA: a company of Italian mercenaries, led by a *condottiere*.

CORONEL: the head of a tilting lance, usually with three or more prongs; from Latin "corona"=crown (because of its shape).

CRINET: the neck armor of a knight's horse; from French "crin"= mane.

CRUPPER: the armor for the hind quarters of a knight's horse.

CUIRASS: Body armor consisting of breast- and backplate.

DAMASCENING: the decoration of steel surfaces with inlaid gold and silver wires; from the city of Damascus in Syria.

DOUBLET: a jacket worn under armor, equipped with "points" (laces) for tieing on elements of armor.

ENARMES: the handgrips of a shield.

ENSIS: the Roman cavalry sword.

FALCHION: a short single-edged sword.

FALCONET: a light cannon.

FLAMBERG: a two-handed sword with a wavy blade.

FLANCHARD: a piece of horse armor covering the flank.

FRANCISCA: the battle-axe of the Franks, often used as a missile, too.

GAMBESON: a quilted garment worn under armor as a shock absorber.

GLADIUS: the Roman short sword.

GLAIVE: a polearm with a long cutting-edge; from Latin "gladius"= sword.

GORGET: a piece of armor for the throat, in the eighteenth century a badge of rank for officers.

GUIGE: the carrying strap of a shield.

GUISARME: a polearm for hacking and stabbing, with a large curved blade.

HALBERD: a polearm with an axe-like blade, a thrusting-spike, and a hook; from German "Helmbarte"=long-handled axe.

HAUBERK: a mail shirt; from German "Halsberge"=neck cover.

HILT: the grip part of a sword.

HOUNSKULL: a bascinet with a pointed visor; from German "Hundsgugel"=dog's hood (because of the snoutlike outline).

JAZERANT: mail reinforced by small plates, especially popular in Persia, Turkey, and India.

JUPON: a tight-fitting coat worn over the body armor in the fourteenth century, usually emblazoned with the knight's arms.

KATANA: the Japanese long sword.

KETTLE-HAT: a broad-brimmed helmet, a "chapel-de-fer."

LORICA: the body armor of the Roman legionnaires.

MACE: an iron club, used as armor-breaker.

MANGONEL: a throwing engine of the Middle Ages, of similar construction as the "onager" of the Romans.

MISERICORDE: a knightly dagger; from Latin "misericordia"=mercy.

MORGENSTERN: a mace with a spiked head; the word is German, and means "morning star."

MORION: a light helmet with strongly curved brim, particularly popular in Spain.

NASAL: noseguard on early helmets.

ONAGER: a Roman throwing engine; the word means "wild ass," because of its kick.

PARTIZAN: a polearm with a wide double-edged blade and short parrying hooks.

PETARD: a land mine for breaching a gate.

PEYTREL: the chest armor of a knight's horse; from Latin "pectoralis"=for the chest.

PICKADILLS: fabric edging of armor parts to prevent clattering and scratching the polished surfaces. In London the craftsmen who lined armor lived in "Piccadilly Circus."

POINTS: armor laces.

POURPOINT: a quilted jacket worn under armor and equipped with laces (points) for the attachment of the armor. The term is French, and means "for the point."

QUARREL: a crossbow bolt; from French "carreau"=square, because of its diamond-shaped head.

QUEUE: the rear-hook attached to the breastplate of a jousting armor, holding the butt end of the lance in position.

QUILLONS: the cross-guard of a sword.

QUINTAINS: a dummy used in jousting practice. It pivoted on its base when struck, and might hit an unwary jouster with its outstretched arm.

RAPIER: the thrusting sword of the seventeenth century, often with an elaborate hilt.

RICASSO: the uppermost blunted section of a rapier blade; for a better grip in thrusting the forefinger was hooked over the quillons and laid against the ricasso.

SAX, SEAX: a machete-like long-knife, the national weapon of the Saxons. Sometimes called "scramasax"—wound knife.

SCIMITAR: a saber; from Persian "shamshir"=lion's tail, because of its sweeping form.

SERPENTINE: a light cannon; from Italian "little snake."

SPONTOON: a polearm developed from the partizan; worn by eighteenth century officers as a badge of rank.

SQUIRE: a Knight's assistant; from old French "escuyer"=shield bearer.

SWORD NAMES: his sword being his most prized possession, the warrior often called it by a name like a living being. Some of the most famous examples are known from the great stories of chivalry, such as King Arthur's *Excalibur*, Sir Gawain's *Galagan-*

tine, Sir Tristram's *Curtana* that later was supposedly owned by Richard the Lion-Hearted, Charlemagne's *La Joyeuse,* Roland's *Durendal,* Siegfried's *Balmung,* and El Cid's *Tizona.*

THORAX: the bronze cuirass of the ancient Greeks.

TREBUCHET: a siege engine for throwing large stones, working on the counter-weight principle.

TSUBA: the guard-plate of a Japanese sword. The decoration of tsuba was one of the most important fields for a Japanese artist.

TUMBLER: a rotating barrel for cleaning mail shirts; the mail shirt was dropped into it together with a shovelful of sawdust sprinkled with oil, when rotated by a crank the friction of the rings against each other acted as a selfcleaning process.

UNIFORM: was developed in the seventeenth century. The bright colors of old uniforms were necessary for distinction between friend and foe, because the battlefield was much obscured by the heavy smoke of the black powder.

VAMPLATE: the disc-shaped hand-guard of a knight's lance.

WAKIZASHI: a Japanese short sword.

PICTURE CREDITS

TWO-HANDED SWORD: Gift of Prince Albrecht Radziwill, 1928

FALCHION: Gift of Mrs. D. H. Schmidt in memory of Theodore Offerman, 1937

BROADSWORD: Gift of William H. Riggs, 1913

PAGES 82 & 83

CORVINUS CROSSBOW: Rogers Fund, 1925

TAPESTRY (DETAIL): Harris Brisbane Dick Fund, 1935

BOAR SPEAR: Rogers Fund, 1904

BOAR SPEAR WITH PISTOL: Gift of William H. Riggs, 1913

BOAR SPEAR: Gift of William H. Riggs, 1913

HUNTING SWORD: Rogers Fund, 1949

HUNTING SWORD WITH PISTOL: Gift of Jean Jacques Reubell, 1926, in memory of his mother, Julia C. Coster, and of his wife, Adeline E. Post, both of New York City

HUNTING KNIFE: Rogers Fund, 1904

BOAR SWORD: Rogers Fund, 1904

PRINCE OF WALES HUNTING: Pulitzer Fund, 1944

PAGES 84 & 85

MATCHLOCK GUN: The collection of Giovanni P. Morosini, presented by his daughter, Giulia, 1932

WHEELLOCK GUNS: Gift of William H. Riggs, 1913; Gift of Prince Albrecht Radziwill, 1928

SNAPHAUNCE GUN: Gift of Alan Rutherfurd Stuyvesant, 1949

MIGUELET GUN: Rogers Fund, 1916

FLINTLOCK GUN: Collection of Giovanni P. Morosini, presented by his daughter Giulia, 1932

PAGES 86 & 87

CHARLES V PISTOL: Gift of William H. Riggs, 1913

TRIPLE-BARRELED PISTOLS (WENDER): Pulitzer Bequest Fund, 1951

BREECH-LOADING CANNON: Rogers Fund, 1917

DOUBLE SHOT CARBINE (ROMAN CANDLE): Gift of William H. Riggs, 1913

CABASSET: Gift of William H. Riggs, 1913

BARBERINI ARMOR: Baker Fund, 1926

VELASQUEZ, DUKE OF OLIVARES: Fletcher Fund, 1952

PAGE 88

CAVALIER'S STEEL HAT: Bashford Dean Memorial Collection, 1929

MUSKETEER, ILLUSTRATION FROM DE GHEYN: Metropolitan Museum of Art Library

PIKEMAN'S ARMOR: Rogers Fund, 1919

PAGE 89

RIGAUD, PORTRAIT OF MARECHAL LA TOUR: Endowment Fund, 1959

PAGES 90 & 91

SCIMITAR OF MURAD V: Gift of Giulia P. Morosini, 1923, in memory of her father, Giovanni P. Morosini.

TURKISH SHIELD: Bequest of George C. Stone, 1936

TURKISH ARMOR: Rogers Fund, 1904

TURKISH HELMET: Special Fund, 1950

TURKISH PISTOLS: Gift of Giulia P. Morosini, 1923, in memory of her father, Giovanni P. Morosini; Collection of Giovanni P. Morosini, presented by his daughter Giulia, 1932

MINIATURE, ARMY ENTERING CITY: Bequest of George C. Pratt, 1945

PAGE 92

MINIATURE, BATTLE SCENE (CONQUEST OF BAGHDAD): Rogers Fund, 1955

HELMET: Bequest of George C. Stone, 1936

OXHEAD MACE: Bequest of George C. Stone, 1936

SCIMITAR: Bequest of Richard B. Seager, 1926

PAGE 93

HORNED HELMET: John Stoneacre Ellis Collection, gift of Mrs. Ellis and Augustus Van Horne Ellis, 1896

AXE: Bequest of George C. Stone, 1936

TULWAR: Bequest of George C. Stone, 1936

CHESSPIECE: Gift of Gustavus Pfeiffer, 1948

PAGE 94

KHATTAR: Bequest of George C. Stone, 1936

GAUNTLET SWORD: Bequest of George C. Stone, 1936

MINIATURE, NIGHT ATTACK: Rogers Fund, 1918

PAGE 95

KRISSTAND: Bequest of George C. Stone, 1936

KRISS: Fletcher Fund, 1928

KRISS: Collection of Giovanni P. Morosini, presented by his daughter Giulia, 1932

PAGE 96

BRASS HELMET, MORO ARMOR, SULU KLEWANGS: Bequest of George C. Stone, 1936

PAGE 97

SWORDS: Rogers Fund, 1914; Bequest of George C. Stone, 1936

CHINESE CROSSBOW: Bequest of George C. Stone, 1936

PAGE 98

GENERAL'S ARMOR: Bequest of George C. Stone, 1936

VASE WITH WARRIORS: Anonymous gift, 1937

PAGE 99

TSUBA AND SET, MILLET AND QUAIL: Gift of a Trustee, 1917

ARMOR: Gift of Bashford Dean, 1914

PAGES 100 & 101

DAISHO SWORD: The Howard Mansfield Collection, Gift of Howard Mansfield, 1936

TACHI SWORD: Bequest of George C. Stone, 1936

KOSUKA: Gift of a Trustee, 1917

KOSUKA, BATTLE SCENE: Gift of a Trustee, 1917

KOSUKA, FUJIYAMA: Bequest of Mrs. H. O. Havemeyer, 1929

TSUBA, SAMURAI AND CHERRY TREE: The Howard Mansfield Collection, Gift of Howard Mansfield, 1936

ARCHER PRINT: The H. O. Havemeyer Collection, Bequest of Mrs. H. O. Havemeyer, 1929

CEREMONIAL ARROWHEADS: The Giovanni P. Morosini Collection, presented by his daughter Giulia, 1932

GUNNER'S PRINT: Metropolitan Museum of Art Library

PAGE 102

KUNIYOSHI PRINT: Metropolitan Museum of Art Library

CATS AND RATS BATTLE, PRINT: Metropolitan Museum of Art Library

PAGE 103

PORTRAIT OF ANDRE FRENCEOIS ALLOIS DE THEYS DE HERCULES, BY NICOLAS DE LARGILLIERE 1659-1746: Collection of Mr. and Mrs. Charles B. Wrightsman

CD. MARINUS W. EURL, PORTRAIT OF MAJOR WILLETT: Bequest of George Willett Van Nest, 1917

FLINTLOCK PISTOLS: Gift of Prince Albrecht Radziwill, 1928

PAGES 104 & 105

FREDERICK OF PRUSSIA, PRINT: Dick Fund, 1947

OFFICER'S GORGET: Rogers Fund, 1917

LIGHT DRAGOON DISH: Rogers Fund, 1913

OFFICER'S SWORD: Gift of Samuel P. Avery, 1912

AMERICAN POWDER HORN: Gift of Mrs. J. H. Grenville Gilbert, 1939

KENTUCKY RIFLES: Gift of Wilfrid Wood, 1956; Gift of Marion Eppley, 1956

PAGES 106 & 107

MEISSONIER, FRIEDLAND—1807: Gift of Henry Hilton, 1887

NAPOLEONIC GUN: Dick Fund, 1942

ENGLISH PRESENTATION SWORD: Dick Fund, 1942

CASED PISTOLS (PIRMET): Rogers Fund, 1928

PAGES 108 & 109

DRAGOON COLT REVOLVER: Gift of John E. Parsons, 1956

INDIAN FIGHT, RUBBING FROM COLT CYLINDER: Gift of John E. Parsons, 1956

REMINGTON, DRAGOONS—1850: Rogers Fund, 1907

WELLS-FARGO COLT REVOLVER: Gift of John E. Parsons, 1957

STAGECOACH HOLDUP, RUBBING FROM WELLS-FARGO COLT REVOLVER: Gift of John E. Parsons, 1957

REMINGTON, COMING THRU THE RYE: Bequest of Jacob Ruppert, 1939

PAGES 110 & 111

A. DE NEUVILLE, THE SPY: Bequest of Collis P. Huntington, 1925

WINSLOW HOMER, PRISONERS FROM THE FRONT: Gift of Mrs. Frank B. Porter, 1922

REMINGTON, CAVALRY CHARGE ON THE SOUTH PLAINS: Gift of Several Gentlemen, 1911

PAGES 112 & 113

SIEGE ENGINE IN DRAGON SHAPE (VALTURIUS): Metropolitan Museum of Art Library

ARMORED CAR (VALTURIUS): Metropolitan Museum of Art Library

ARMORED SHIP (VALTURIUS): Metropolitan Museum of Art Library

ARMORED SHIP (FIN DE LA GUERRE): Whittelsey Fund, 1959

MONITOR AND MERRIMAC: Whittelsey Fund, 1959

PAGES 114 & 115

GREEK ARMORER MAKING HELMET: Fletcher Fund, 1942

MAXIMILIAN IN HIS ARMOR SHOP: Metropolitan Museum of Art Library

Metropolitan Museum of Art armor shop